Going Into Space

GOING INTO SPACE

by Arthur C. Clarke

Illustrated with photographs and diagrams

HARPER & BROTHERS, NEW YORK

Contents

List of Plates

(Plates will be found in a group following page 22)

List of Figures

Going Into Space

1 - Voyages in Space

MAN is the great explorer. Perhaps a million years ago, our remote ancestors began to spread over the face of the world until at last they had made their homes in every continent except the frozen Antarctic. The final chapter in the long story of Earth's exploration was not written until our own age. Now, thanks to the conquest of the air, no spot on the globe is more than a few hours' distance from any other, and soon it will be possible to circle the world inside a single day.

It is hard for us to remember that, only fifty years ago, there were great areas of the Earth where no man had ever been. Our grandfathers could dream, when they read such adventure stories as *King Solomon's Mines*, of strange countries and peoples still waiting to be discovered. Now that the airplane is rapidly filling in the last blanks on the map, the mystery and romance which always surround the unknown have been swept away. The world is a more humdrum and a less exciting place.

Or so it seems at first sight. The truth of the matter is that, although we may have explored the continents, we have scarcely scratched the surface even of our own

planet. The ocean deeps—three quarters of the Earth—
are still as unknown as was Darkest Africa a century ago.
And in the other direction, above the atmosphere, lies the
enormous emptiness of space. Shining out there in the
darkness we can see other worlds than ours—the Moon,
the planets, and the still more distant stars. Not long ago,
it seemed that only dreams could reach them. "Crying for
the Moon" meant asking for something that was utterly
impossible. In the past generation, all that has changed.
We know now, in theory at least, how we may escape
from our native world and go voyaging out into space.
When men have imagined something, sooner or later they
have always done it, as the discovery of flight has proved.
For the same reason, since we now have the means to
travel into space, it is only a matter of time before the first
Columbus of the future sets course for the Moon.

The development of the rocket during the Second World
War has made it possible to talk seriously about voyages
to the planets. Later in this book we will see what rockets
have already achieved, and what still remains to be done
before we can construct real spaceships. But first of all,
let us look for a moment into the past to find out how the
idea of interplanetary flight first arose.

In ancient times, before the invention of the telescope,
no one knew that there *were* any other worlds besides
our own. There were many theories to explain the Sun,
Moon, and stars, but there was no way of proving which
of them was correct. If you go out at night under a clear
sky and look up at the heavens, you would never be able
to guess—if someone had not already told you!—that
those twinkling points of light were blazing suns, most of

them millions of times larger than the world on which we live. Such an idea seems against all common sense, so it is not surprising that it was a long time before anyone could prove it was true, and longer still before everybody else believed them.

Even the Moon, our nearest neighbor, is too far away for the unaided eye to tell us much about it, though some of the Greek scientists more than two thousand years ago had been able to make a good estimate of its size. They knew that it must be a world of its own, and not just a small globe only a few miles away; but what kind of a world it was, they could not tell.

The invention of the telescope changed all this. A century before, Columbus had discovered a new world in the West, and the First Elizabethan Age had seen the great explorations of such adventurers as Drake and Raleigh. Then, in 1609, the Italian scientist Galileo looked through his crude, home-made telescopes and discovered new lands in the sky. Although the best instrument Galileo used was not as good as a pair of modern field glasses, he could see the mountains and plains on the Moon and was even able to map its surface. After that date, men knew definitely that the Earth was not the only world that existed, and they also began to wonder if we were the only people in the universe. To *that* question, we still do not know the answer—but one day we will.

It is not surprising that the discoveries of Galileo and later astronomers excited enormous interest. Men began to ask themselves what it was like in the new lands they could dimly see through their feeble telescopes. They tried to imagine the kinds of creatures that might live there.

And, before long, they started wondering if explorers would ever be able to cross space as they had already crossed the sea.

This, remember, was three hundred years ago. We think of space-flight as a modern idea, and so it is rather startling to discover that several stories of voyages to the Moon (and the Sun!) were written by the French author Cyrano de Bergerac as long ago as 1656. Plate 1, taken from Cyrano's *Voyages to the Moon and Sun,* shows what may well be considered as the first of all imaginary spaceships. Like many other spaceships in fiction since that day, I am afraid it wouldn't have worked. The idea was that burning glasses would concentrate the sun's rays into the sphere in which Cyrano is sitting, and that the heated air would then rush out and drive the vehicle upwards by a form of jet-propulsion! All that would have happened in practice, of course, is that Cyrano would soon have been cooked by the concentrated sunlight, but the sphere wouldn't have budged. And today we know that there is no air between us and the Moon, so such an arrangement couldn't possibly have worked once it left the atmosphere.

During the next two hundred years, many other writers produced tales of journeys to the Moon, but few of them were intended at all seriously. At the same time, astronomical knowledge steadily increased. A good deal had been discovered about the Earth's atmosphere—that invisible blanket which enables us to breathe and which protects us from space—and the forces which make the planets move were better understood.

The first man to use all this new knowledge was the famous French writer Jules Verne, who foresaw so many of our modern inventions, such as the submarine and the helicopter. His novel *From the Earth to the Moon,* which was published in 1865, contained a remarkable amount of accurate scientific information, and is still well worth reading today (much of it is also highly amusing). Verne knew that nothing depending upon the air could possibly fly to the Moon, so that ruled out balloons and machines using wings or propellers. But if one could build an enormous gun, and fire a shell from it in the right direction *and* with enough speed, it would be possible to hit the Moon. It is not hard to calculate what starting speed the shell would need or how long the journey would take, and Verne was very careful to get all his figures right. Where he let his imagination go, however, was in pretending that men could travel in such a shell without being killed by the concussion when the gun was fired, no matter how well padded and protected they might be.

And there was another objection to Verne's mammoth gun, not so well known in his time as it is today. As experiments in supersonic flight have shown, anything moving through our atmosphere at very high speeds meets tremendous resistance, and so becomes very hot. For this reason, the fastest jet planes now have to be fitted with refrigeration. But Jules Verne's shell would have traveled *thirty* times as fast as any jet flying today. It would not simply have become hot—it would have melted almost immediately, even before it left the barrel of the gun! (Plate 2.)

However, though we of today may pick holes in his story, Verne's ideas were brilliantly worked out and they must have made many people think seriously about travel

through space. The shell inside which his voyagers circled
the Moon was fitted with apparatus to supply oxygen,
observation windows through which the travelers could
watch the stars, and—the most modern touch of all—
rockets for steering. Almost a hundred years ago, Verne
realized that rockets could be used to give a "push" in the
vacuum of space, something that many people do not
understand even today, though, as you will see later, the
reason for it is very simple.

Since Jules Verne's time, there have been thousands of
stories about space-flight, only a few of them at all accurate
scientifically, and fewer still of any importance as works
of literature. Much the best from the latter point of view
is H. G. Wells's *The First Men in the Moon*, though it
was written as long ago as 1901, two years before the first
airplane left the ground. It conveys beautifully the wonder
and mystery of other worlds, and you will never forget
Wells's description of the lunar dawn, or his hero's adventures in the buried empire of the "Selenites." It is true
that the Moon, as we know today, is somewhat different
from the planet which Wells imagined. Yet I think that
men will still be reading his book with enjoyment long
after they have traveled to much more distant worlds!

Wells used neither guns nor rockets to carry his travelers
safely across space. His scientist, Cavor, invented a wonderful substance which acted as a screen to gravity—the
force which gives us our weight—just as a piece of dark
glass can screen out light. Anything surrounded by this
"Cavorite" lost its weight and, since the Earth could no
longer hold it down, went sailing up into the sky. So
Wells's spaceship was simply a large sphere entirely cov-

ered with Cavorite screens which could be opened or closed as required. If you wanted to go to the Moon, you opened the screen on the Moonward side of the sphere, and you were attracted in that direction. It was as simple as that!

I am afraid that anyone who devotes his life to the search for Cavorite will be starting on a wild-goose chase. It is quite easy to show that a gravity-screen of this kind could not possibly exist. One day, perhaps, we *may* be able to control gravity in some fashion. But it will need a great deal of power to do so, and certainly would not be managed simply by opening and closing the blinds!

That need not worry us unduly, for we do not require any wonderful new inventions to enable us to reach the planets. The tool for the job has been known for over seven hundred years, since the Chinese made the first gunpowder rockets around the year 1200. But until recent times, the rocket was little more than a firework, its main practical use being for shooting lines to shipwrecked mariners. During the nineteenth century it was employed as a weapon for a short period, but when more accurate guns were built war rockets soon became obsolete. They played no important part at all in the 1914-1918 War.

There are many reasons why interest in the rocket revived from 1920 onwards. In the first place, Man had now conquered the air and so achieved one of his oldest dreams. Flying had always been considered impossible by most people: when the Wright brothers started to make their first short hops in 1903, newspaper editors refused to print the story because they *knew* it couldn't be true!

Yet now, after 1920, airplanes were flying all over the world. After the air, the next step could only be—Space.

But space was airless, so some new form of engine would have to be used, an engine that would carry *all* its fuel and wouldn't have to "push" against something outside it in order to move forward. An airplane can reach only a certain height, usually less than ten miles, because it depends on the atmosphere around it in several ways. In the first place, the fuel it carries could not burn without the oxygen in the air; the motor would "suffocate," just as you would under the same conditions. The wings would have nothing to work upon, for it is the air flowing around them that supports the plane. And, of course, the controls would be equally useless. It makes very little difference whether the aircraft is driven by propellers or jets; its ceiling is strictly limited owing to the thinness of the upper atmosphere. The greatest height ever reached by an airplane not using rockets is eleven and a half miles.

Balloons, floating in the air like a cork on water, can do considerably better than this. If they are carrying only small loads, they can reach heights of 25 miles before the air can no longer support them. At this altitude, the air is so thin that, even if it were compressed a hundredfold, it would not be as dense as it is down here at sea level. Beyond this region, only rockets can ever fly.

Although, as we have already seen, Jules Verne knew this back in 1865, few scientists gave the rocket any serious thought until the end of the First World War. Even then, it was first looked upon merely as a way of sending automatic instruments far above the Earth, as had already been done with balloons. The idea that it could carry men as well was, for a long time, rather too fantastic to accept, but by 1930 nearly everyone knew that if we ever *did* succeed in building spaceships, they would be rocket-propelled.

During the last few years, in fact, the words *rocket* and *spaceship* have almost gone together. Even before it has happened, the world has started to take space-flight for granted! One result of this has been a flood of stories and films on the subject, most of them not at all accurate scientifically, even though they are often quite entertaining.

Two of Hollywood's most elegant spaceships are shown in Plates 3, 4, and 5, and many millions of people have probably been influenced by these designs. As we shall see later, some types of spaceship may indeed look something like this, but the ships which will take us on really long voyages to the planets will be very different indeed, even though they will still be rocket-propelled.

The man who did most to draw attention to the possibilities of rocket-flight was a Rumanian-born mathematician, Professor Hermann Oberth (Plate 6), who had become interested in space-flight while he was still a student and had devoted all his spare time to investigating its problems. In his books he was able to show that there was nothing impossible about space-travel, *if* one could use the right kinds of fuel and carry enough of them. Oberth did little actual experimenting; nearly all his work was with pencil and paper. However, it laid the foundations for almost everything that happened afterwards.

Before any invention can progress from a sketch on paper to a machine that actually works, many tests and experiments are needed. The laws of aeronautics had been known for almost a hundred years before the Wrights made their first successful flying machine. Conquering space would be an even more difficult task, and the first step that had to be taken was to make more efficient and more powerful rockets than had ever been built before.

And so we come to a chapter of history which opened in the years when Hitler was making himself master of Germany, and which ended a little more than ten years later when the first V-2's began to climb towards the frontiers of space.

2 - From Firework to V-2

THERE are two different kinds of rocket, one of which has been in existence for more than seven hundred years, while the second was born just before the last War. Everyone knows the old-fashioned variety which goes soaring skywards in such numbers on Guy Fawkes' Night in Great Britain and Independence Day in the United States. This is the familiar powder rocket, consisting simply of a hollow tube packed with a type of slow-burning gunpowder. There is a small nozzle at the end of the tube, made in the cheap cardboard variety merely by pinching the walls of the cylinder together. As the powder burns, a great volume of gas is produced, which comes rushing out of the nozzle at a high speed and drives the rocket upwards. The rocket, in fact, was the first jet-propelled vehicle! And although we will spend some time later seeing exactly how this method of propulsion works, it might be a good idea to correct one very common mistake right now. The rocket does *not*, as so many people still imagine, move forward because the hot exhaust gases "press on the air behind." In fact, it works much better when there is *no* air behind—in other words, out in space.

The powder rocket, though it is so simple to manufacture, has a number of serious disadvantages. In the first place, there is no control over the thrust or push produced, once burning has started. It would not be very convenient to have a car which ran at full speed until the fuel tank was empty, and had no throttle at all!

Secondly, such solid-propellant rockets, as they are called, are very inefficient. Explosives like gunpowder can produce impressive bangs, but they actually contain a good deal less energy than the same weight of liquid fuels, such as gasoline or alcohol.

To make better rockets, therefore, it was necessary to abandon the old design and the old propellants, and to develop real "rocket motors" which would burn liquids pumped into them from outside. Such rockets could be started or stopped as required, and by the use of properly designed nozzles and combustion chambers much better performances could be obtained than were ever possible with the old powder rockets.

The original type of rocket is, however, by no means extinct, altogether apart from its use as a firework. The vast majority of rocket weapons now employed in warfare, such as those launched from aircraft, are of this kind. They have also been employed for the jet-assisted take-off of heavily loaded aircraft, but as it seems very unlikely that solid-propellant rockets will be used in space-flight, we will not refer to them again.*

* *Warning!* It is dangerous, and also against the law, to attempt to make powder rockets. Anyone wishing to experiment should buy commercially built rockets such as the well-known Jetex, Dyna-Jet, or Minijet motors. Liquid-propellant rockets require elaborate safety precautions and no amateur should attempt to construct and use them. Even experts have been killed by rockets of both types!

The first liquid-propellant rocket motors were built in the United States soon after the First World War by Professor Robert H. Goddard, a brilliant but very shy scientist (Plate 7). He published hardly any of his results, probably because of the wild newspaper comments which always followed accounts of rocket experimenting back in the 1920's—or, for that matter, at much later dates.

\ Consequently, very little was known about Goddard's work, and experiments in Europe went on independently. The men carrying them out were a group of young Germans, with very little money but great enthusiasm. Just outside Berlin, during the years 1927 to 1933, they built numerous small rocket motors which they first tested on the ground and then flew to heights of a few thousand feet, landing them again by parachute.

These experiments attracted a great deal of publicity, but much more important was the fact that they really laid the foundations of rocket engineering as we know it today, and provided the training for the men who were later, with the support of the German Army, to build the V-2.

It is a sad fact that only in time of war can scientists obtain support for their more imaginative ideas. Radar, jet-propulsion, atomic energy, and rockets might not have reached their present stage of development even in a hundred years of peace. But at the great German research centre of Peenemünde, on the shores of the Baltic, the rocket grew from a toy to a giant missile taller than a house—all in less than ten years.

The man who directed the V-2 project, Dr. Wernher von Braun (Plate 8), had become fascinated by the idea of space-travel while he was a boy, and had worked with the German Rocket Society when he was still in his teens. Next to radar and the atom bomb, the V-2 was the greatest scientific achievement of the War. It could carry a ton of explosives more than 200 miles in less than five minutes.

Most of the V-2's flight was unpowered: it built up speed by the thrust of its rocket motor for the first minute, and thereafter coasted under its momentum for the rest of the journey, which lasted another four minutes. Since most of its flight-path was at altitudes of over twenty miles, there was practically no air resistance to slow it down.

This brings us to a most important point. When we start anything moving here on Earth—a car, a boat, a stone rolling along the ground—friction very quickly brings it to rest. To keep the object on the move, we have to continue to apply some force.

This is no longer true in space, where there is no friction of any kind. The planets move round the Sun at speeds of many thousands of miles an hour—but there's nothing to slow them down, so they'll keep on traveling forever. In the same way, a rocket launched beyond the Earth could travel through space for eternity, without using a drop of fuel.

However, the V-2's speed of 3,500 m.p.h. was far too low to let it escape from Earth. After a few minutes, the steady pull of gravity was able to check its upward flight. Like any other object thrown up into the air, the rocket had to fall back eventually, following the curve which mathematicians call an ellipse. By adjusting the speed which the V-2 reached, its range could be varied, just as one can throw a ball for varying distances by altering the force of one's throw.

Dr. von Braun was only 30 when the first V-2 was launched after some several hundred million dollars had been spent on its development. Even then more than 60,000 alterations to the design had to be made before it could be used in military operations. These figures will give some idea of the cost of large-scale rocket research —and the building of spaceships will be even more expensive.

The V-2 (Plates 9 and 11) was a tremendous advance over anything that had gone before, and came as a great surprise to most people outside Germany. Before it could be built, many smaller rockets had been fired to test the thousands of different devices which were incorporated in the final missile. For although the rocket motor itself seems such a simple arrangement, many complicated accessories are needed to insure that it works properly (Figure 1).

First, of course, are the tanks for the propellants. The fuel used in the V-2 was alcohol, and the rocket carried no less than four tons of this in a large aluminum tank. But a fuel won't burn by itself; it needs oxygen. Other types of engines get their oxygen from the surrounding air; the rocket, however, carries its supply along with it. The V-2 therefore had a second tank holding nearly five tons of *liquid* oxygen. (The old powder rockets also contain oxygen, but combined chemically in such substances as saltpeter.)

The next problem was to get the alcohol and oxygen from the tanks into the motor where they would be burned. This might seem a rather simple matter—until one realizes the rate at which a large rocket uses up its propellants. In

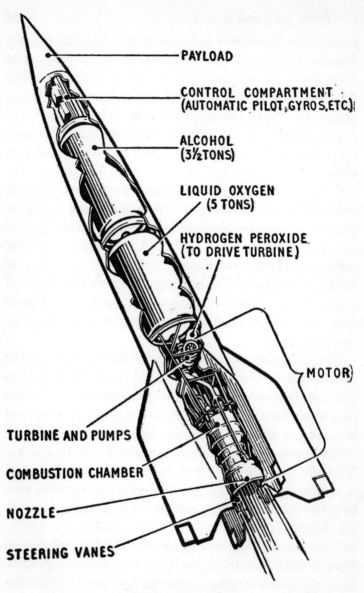

PAYLOAD

CONTROL COMPARTMENT
(AUTOMATIC PILOT,GYROS,ETC.)

ALCOHOL
(3½TONS)

LIQUID OXYGEN
(5 TONS)

HYDROGEN PEROXIDE
(TO DRIVE TURBINE)

MOTOR

TURBINE AND PUMPS

COMBUSTION CHAMBER

NOZZLE

STEERING VANES

Fig. 1. V-2 rocket.

the case of the V-2, the rate was *one ton every eight seconds!* Building pumps to handle this rate of flow was in itself a major engineering achievement. The V-2 pumps were driven by a little steam turbine which could be held in both hands yet developed over 500 horsepower.

The steam needed to drive the turbine was produced in a very ingenious manner. You may know the chemical called hydrogen peroxide, which is widely used for bleaching. The variety sold in the shops is actually 95 per cent water, which is just as well. For hydrogen peroxide breaks down very easily into oxygen and water, producing a large amount of heat as it does so. You can see this even with the household variety, which is continually giving off bubbles of oxygen. The pure substance, however, decomposes very rapidly when certain chemicals are added to it, generating so much heat that large quantities of steam are produced.

It was this steam that was used to drive the turbine pumps of the V-2. The reaction is so powerful, in fact, that hydrogen peroxide has been used by itself as a rocket propellant. The world's first rocket-driven fighter, the Messerschmitt 163, was peroxide-powered.

The heart of any rocket vehicle is, of course, the motor itself, which has to handle enormous forces and very high temperatures. The V-2 motor, though it was only five feet long, developed more than twice the horsepower of a giant liner like the *Queen Elizabeth!* This means that it had to be very carefully designed, for if anything went wrong there would almost certainly be a tremendous explosion. True, the V-2 designers wanted to produce an explosion —but at the end of the flight, not at the beginning!

A modern rocket motor consists of two main parts: the combustion chamber and the nozzle. The propellants—in the case of the V-2, alcohol and liquid oxygen—are pumped into the combustion chamber and ignited either electrically or by some other means. Once the propellants have started to burn, the motor will continue to run as long as fuel and oxygen are pumped into it. Because of the heat produced, the liquids one starts with are turned instantly into huge volumes of gas (mostly steam and carbon dioxide) which rush out through the nozzle.

The job the nozzle does is, to put it rather roughly, to see that the hot exhaust gases leave the rocket all moving in the same direction and at the greatest possible speed. The more efficiently the nozzle does its work, the greater the thrust or "push" that the rocket will produce.

The V-2 motor, which is still one of the largest rocket motors ever built, gave a thrust of nearly 30 tons. Thus, if it had been mounted vertically, it would have been able to lift the weight of 350 full-grown men. It is sometimes hard to realize that such enormous forces can be produced by nothing more than a jet of gas, yet, when one considers what damage gales and hurricanes can do, it is perhaps not so surprising. In the fiercest of hurricanes, the wind speed may exceed 100 m.p.h.—but the speed of the gases in the V-2 jet is 4,500 m.p.h.

A large rocket is of no use unless you can make it go in the required direction, and the V-2 was not merely aimed like a gun but was actually steered in flight just like an airplane. Although it had fins, these were useless in the thin air of the upper atmosphere and a new method of steering had to be devised, a method which, incidentally, can also be used to steer spaceships when they fly out into the vacuum between the planets.

Fixed to the body of the V-2 were two pairs of little vanes or rudders, which lay in the path of the exhaust gases. Normally these vanes were edge-on, as it were, to the jet. If they were tilted, however, the pressure of the jet against them would slew the rocket around and so it could be steered in any desired direction—up or down, right or left.

Rockets can also be steered by tilting the entire motor and thus swinging the jet around. This is a more complicated method, but it has been successfully used in one large American missile, *Viking* (Plate 12).

Tanks—pumps—motor—these are the basic units of any modern liquid-propellant rocket. In addition, there are many valves and seals, and masses of piping, to make sure that the various liquids flow in the right directions and at the correct rates. There may also be, according to the job the rocket is designed to do, complicated control devices and automatic pilots. Sometimes these are operated from self-contained electronic "brains" in the rocket, and sometimes they are controlled by radio impulses from ground stations. It is not at all surprising, therefore, that a large rocket costs tens of thousands of dollars.

The first V-2 was launched in 1942, but fortunately for England another two years were needed before it was ready to be used. Even then it still had many flaws, and half the V-2's fired never reached their targets. The 1,115 which did reach London killed about 3,000 people.

To understand how the V-2 operated, let's go back for a moment to the spring of 1945, to the closing days of the

War. The place is Holland, not far from The Hague. You're
looking along an avenue of trees stretching into the distance on either side of a narrow lane. It's a peaceful, rustic
scene, and there is absolutely no sign of life.

Yet there has been heavy traffic along this road—there
are broad tire-marks everywhere—and what are those
curious concrete slabs set in the ground at regular inter-
vals? You look around you—and *now* you understand why
the place is so deserted. For, standing on one of the concrete slabs, so close that you can see the slight wrinkles
in its metal skin, is a V-2 waiting to be launched against
London. The alcohol and oxygen tanks have already been
filled: the tire-marks were made by the heavy tank-trucks
when they drove away. In a hidden dugout close at hand,
the launching crew is waiting for the signal to fire.

There's a sudden rumbling roar as vapor gushes from
the nozzle of the rocket. The pumps have started; alcohol
and oxygen are pouring into the combustion chamber. A
moment later, with a screaming thunder that seems to
shake earth and sky, the jet is ignited and flame bursts
forth from the base of the rocket. Yet it does not move:
the motor is still throttled back and the thrust is not yet
powerful enough to lift the missile.

A few seconds later, when the firing commander has
satisfied himself that everything is working properly, he
switches to full power. The rocket lifts from its supporting
table, while flames splash around it in all directions. It's
going up—oh, so slowly and gracefully—balanced on that
roaring, white-hot pillar of gas. That slow, steady rise is
the most surprising thing about the launch; it almost looks
as if the rocket is on an invisible elevator. But it gains

speed quickly—already it's a thousand feet up, accelerating away from Earth more rapidly than anything ever fell *towards* it under gravity. And now it's dwindling into the sky, climbing almost vertically, but veering just a little to the west—towards London, more than two hundred miles away . . .

If you were in that rocket, what would you see and hear? You'd leave most of the sound behind you; you'd see the Earth snatched away, the woods and fields shrink behind, the landscape widen, towns and cities and coast line dwindle below, clouds whip past and be gone in an instant. Sixty seconds after take-off, hurled upwards by more than 600,000 horsepower, the rocket would be moving at a mile a second, its fuel tanks almost empty. Nine tons of alcohol and oxygen have raced through its motor in just over a minute.

Now the motor's cutting out—it's done its job. For the rest of the journey, the rocket will be moving under gravity alone, just as a shell does when it has left the gun.

We're now twenty miles above the Earth, still climbing, no longer vertically, but at an angle of 45 degrees, for the automatic pilot in the control compartment has now done its work. The sound you can hear coming through the walls of the rocket is the thin air rushing past at thirty-five hundred miles an hour. As we climb towards the edge of the atmosphere, even this will die away into the utter and everlasting silence of space.

Look at the sky above. It's quite black, for there's no more air to scatter the sunlight. The familiar blue vault of heaven is already far below us. Overhead, the brighter stars are shining, even though it's daytime and the sun is visible down there in the south.

Forty miles up, we're still rising, though more slowly now. Spread out beneath us like a giant map lie all the countries of western Europe, curving down to the misty horizon six hundred miles away. A storm is coming in from the Atlantic, and we can see its cloud banks covering Wales and Ireland with a gleaming layer of white. To the south, we can look across Switzerland far down into Italy, but the only sign of the Alps is a bright patch that might easily be mistaken for cloud. We are so high that even the greatest mountains are flattened into the landscape.

And now the rocket has reached the peak of its flight. Sixty miles above the Earth, halfway across the North Sea, it has ceased to climb, and for a brief instant it is traveling horizontally. If it could maintain this speed and height it could cross the Atlantic in less than an hour— but already it is beginning to drop down the long slope to London, still a hundred miles away. And as it falls, it starts to gain speed once more. If you could count the miles remaining before the target is reached, they would pass so swiftly that there would scarcely be time to pause for breath between them: 95 . . . 94 . . . 93 . . . 92 . . .

The million and a half square miles we could see from the highest point of the flight is slowly contracting as we sink again to earth. Behind us, central Europe has dropped below the edge of the horizon; ahead, only part of Ireland is still visible. Yet, though the rocket is falling back to earth, its nose is still pointing to the stars overhead. Since there is practically no air resistance to act on the fins, there's nothing to make the missile turn into the

1. Cyrano de Bergerac's "ramjet."

2. Jules Verne's space-gun.

3. Spaceship on Moon (from the motion picture *Destination Moon,* courtesy of Eagle-Lion).

4. Building the spaceship (from the motion picture *When Worlds Collide*, courtesy of Paramount Productions).

5. Launching the spaceship (from the motion picture *When Worlds Collide*, courtesy of Paramount Productions).

6. Professor Hermann Oberth.
(Photograph by A. C. Clarke)

7. Professor Robert Goddard.
(Photograph: American Rocket
Society)

8. Dr. Wernher von Braun.
(Photograph by A. C. Clarke)

9. V-2 rocket on trailer. (Photograph by A. C. Clarke)

10. Rocket motor under test.

11. V-2 being prepared for launching at White Sands Proving Ground. (Photograph: Applied Physics Laboratory, Johns Hopkins University)

12. *Viking* rocket.

13. V-2—*WAC Corporal* step-rocket at take-off.

14. Mice under free-fall conditions. (Photograph: U.S. Department of Defense)

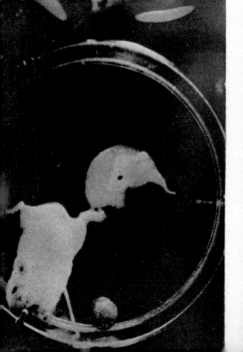
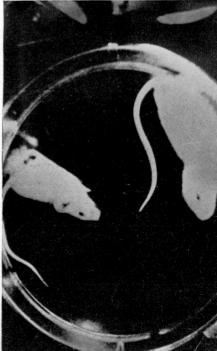

15. Douglas *Skyrocket*.

16. Refueling lunar spaceshi[p]
from tanker rocket. (Painting b[y]
G. A. Frodsham)

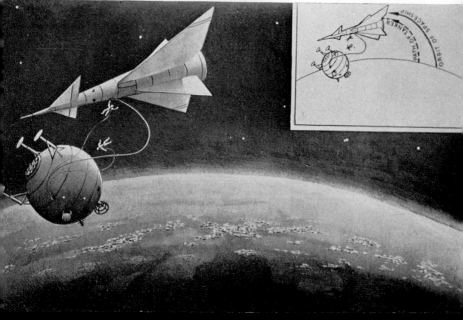

17. Spacesuit (from the motion picture *Destination Moon,* courtesy of Eagle-Lion).

18. High-altitude pressure suit. (Photograph: Air Research and Development Command)

19. The Earth from 100 miles up, looking across the western United States to the Gulf of California. (Official U. S. Navy photograph)

20. Space-station. (Design: Dr. Wernher von Braun)

21. Space-station. (Drawing by R. A. Smith)

22. The Moon: 7 days old
(Lick Observatory photograph)

23. The Moon: South Pole (Mount
Wilson and Palomar observatories).

24. Lunar prospectors. (Drawing by R. A. Smith)

25. 250-foot radio telescope. (Courtesy of Husband & Co., consulting engineers, and Professor A. C. B. Lovell, Department of Radio Astronomy, Manchester University)

26. Space-liner. (Drawing by R. A. Smith)

27. Jupiter, showing Great Red Spot, satellite Ganymede and shadow. (Photograph by 200-inch Hale reflector, courtesy Mount Wilson and Palomar observatories)

28. Saturn. (Photograph by 100-inch reflector, courtesy Mount Wilson and Palomar observatories)

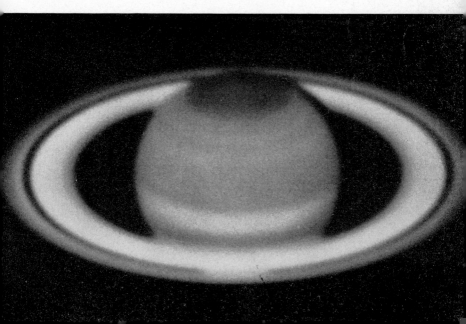

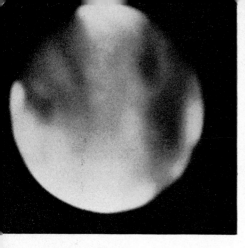
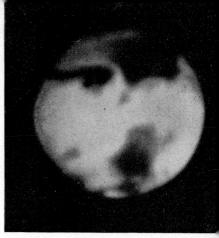

29. Mars, photographed in blue (left) and red (right) light. (Photograph by 200-inch Hale reflector, courtesy Mount Wilson and Palomar observatories)

30. Pressure domes. (Photograph by A. C. Clarke)

direction of flight. At the moment, indeed, it's actually moving *sideways* through space. Not until it enters the lower atmosphere again will the air rushing past veer the rocket around towards the target.

We've only forty miles to go now, and the speed is mounting rapidly. Listen! The silence of space has ended; around us now is a faint whistle of air, rising second by second to a screaming roar. We're coming back into the stratosphere, far more swiftly than we rose through it on the way up. The pressure of air on the fins is swinging the rocket round, aiming it towards the heart of the city. The air resistance is swiftly rising; like a meteor, the rocket is becoming heated by the tremendous friction. Already the steel nose is glowing red-hot . . . less than ten miles to go now . . .

And so, at three times the speed of sound, the first of the giant rockets descended upon London on September 8th, 1944. The V-2 was developed as a weapon of war, yet the knowledge and the experience that were gathered during its building set our feet firmly on the road to space. Let us hope that, by a long future of peaceful service, the rocket can atone for its original misuse.

3 - How the Rocket Works

WE HAVE now had a look at the history of the rocket, and have some idea of the elaborate machinery that goes into a great missile like the V-2. However, we are not interested in the use of rockets as weapons, but as vehicles to take men into the airless reaches beyond the atmosphere. So, before we go any further, let's make sure that we understand why it is that the rocket, unlike all other forms of propulsion, can still work when there is no air around it.

All forms of movement are the result of pushing or pulling on something. When you walk, your feet push against the ground. If the ground were perfectly smooth so that you could get no grip on it, movement would be impossible—as anyone who has tried walking on ice will agree! Locomotives and motorcars depend for their movement on the friction of the wheels against whatever supports them: the road surface or the rails. Without this friction, the wheels would spin round but the vehicles would get nowhere.

Ships and propeller-driven aircraft rely on screws which

can act on the medium around them, water in one case, air in the other. With no air or water, they too would be helpless.

Yet a rocket out in space has nothing around it; in fact, it is in a better vacuum than any we can make on Earth. So how can it possibly move if, as it seems, it has "nothing to push against"?

The answer is really quite simple. The rocket carries with it something that it *can* push against: its fuel! This example should make the principle clear.

Imagine that you were out in space, and that floating beside you was some large, heavy object. If you could brace yourself against this object and then give a good kick, you would move off in one direction and the object would move off in the other. It would have given you something to push against; moreover, if its weight (or strictly speaking, its mass) were the same as yours, it would move in one direction at exactly the same speed as you moved in the other.

Now picture a rocket in the same sort of situation. It's a massive body, and perhaps three quarters of it consists of fuel. (The 13-ton V-2, remember, carried 4 tons of alcohol and 5 tons of oxygen, 9 tons altogether.) This fuel is pumped into the combustion chamber, where it burns violently and continuously. As a result, the burnt gases (280 pounds of them every second in the V-2) are "kicked" down the nozzle at thousands of miles an hour. It's that kick, *inside* the rocket motor, which moves the whole rocket forward. As long as there is fuel to burn, it will continue to gain speed.

What happens to the burnt exhaust gases once they

have left the rocket doesn't matter in the least. The only effect that any surrounding air could have would be to slow down the escaping gases and thus to *reduce* the thrust or push of the motor. The rocket's performance, therefore, steadily improves as it climbs out of the atmosphere.

This, then, is why the rocket is so important, not only for space-travel, but for high-altitude flight in our own atmosphere, where there is some air, though not enough for jets or propellers to work properly. You'll see, moreover, that rocket motors can be used not only for propulsion in space but, what is equally important, for steering and navigation as well.

Once we understand how the rocket works, we can see that the speed it is capable of reaching (forgetting for the moment about the effects of gravity and air resistance) depends on two things. The most important of these is the speed with which the gases come out of the nozzle, the exhaust velocity, to give it its proper name. If you could double the exhaust velocity of a rocket's jet, you'd enable the rocket itself to reach twice as great a speed.

The other important factor is, of course, the actual amount of propellants the rocket can carry. The larger we can make the tanks, and the lighter the empty weight of the rocket, the greater its final speed when all the fuel is burnt. About the best we have been able to do so far is to build rockets that were four times as heavy when full of propellants as when empty. If you'll think about it for a moment, you'll realize that means that three quarters of the weight of the rocket was alcohol and oxygen, so that the remaining one quarter had to cover everything else—tanks, motor, controls, structure, *and* cargo or payload. Rockets, therefore, differ from all other forms of transport in this respect. The weight of the gasoline in an automobile is only a very small fraction of the machine's total weight. Even for a heavily loaded, long-distance bomber, the fuel weight will rarely be more than half the aircraft's total weight. The rocket, of course, has the disadvantage of having to carry along not only its fuel but the oxygen to burn it in as well. Still, the handicap is worth it, for it gives the rocket the freedom of space.

There's still another very important respect in which long-distance rockets—and spaceships, when we start building them—differ from the forms of transport we use on Earth. Automobiles, locomotives, and aircraft travel at a fairly constant speed, with their motors running all the time. Partly for reasons of fuel economy, rockets will operate on a very different principle.

We have already seen that the V-2's launched against England ran their motors only for the first minute of their flight. That was as long as the fuel lasted—but at the end of that time the great missiles had gained enough speed to coast the remainder of their journey, which lasted another four minutes.

The same sort of thing will happen on space voyages, except that the differences in times will be much more striking. A spaceship climbing away from the Earth might run its motors for less than ten minutes—and in that short time would have acquired sufficient speed to glide, silently and effortlessly, without using any more fuel, on a journey through outer space that might last for months.

When an aircraft designer makes plans for an airplane with a certain range, he has to make sure that there's enough fuel to keep the motors running for the whole length of the trip—and with something to spare. He's concerned, therefore, with endurance or flying time. A rocket or spaceship designer, on the other hand, is chiefly worried about the speed his vehicle will reach when it has burnt all its propellants—and the quicker it burns them the better, because then it won't have to carry along any unnecessary weight. For any given flight or mission, there's a certain critical speed. Once the rocket has reached this, it doesn't matter if its fuel tanks are empty. If it started off in the right direction, it will cover the rest of the distance automatically under its own momentum and the influence of gravity.

The reason we've not been able to make any space voyages so far is because the necessary speeds are so high. A rocket that merely had to escape from the gravity pull of Earth, without doing anything else, like landing on another planet, would have to reach a speed of no less than 25,000 miles an hour, or 7 miles a second, before power was cut off. The V-2 rocket attained a speed of about a mile a second. We will, therefore, have to build rockets capable of traveling seven times as fast as this before we can even send anything away from the Earth —let alone think about getting it safely back again.

One very important way of tackling this problem is by means of what is known as the step-rocket. If we arrange things so that one rocket carries another on its nose, and the two separate as soon as the larger rocket has exhausted all its fuel, then clearly the smaller missile will start with a considerable initial speed and can go on, using its own fuel, to reach even higher velocities. Indeed, *if* you could build a rocket with enough steps or stages, there would be no limit to the final speed you could reach with the last and smallest stage, when all the others had dropped off. In practice, three stages are about the most we can economically expect to use.

The famous fable of the eagle and the wren illustrates the step principle perfectly. The wren, you may remember, boasted that it could fly higher than the eagle. It proved this by hiding in the eagle's feathers, waiting until the giant bird had exhausted itself reaching its ceiling, and then flying on by itself to achieve victory, having done no work at all for most of the way.

To see how the step principle might work in practice, let's take a very simple example. Imagine that a V-2 carried up a little scale model of itself, weighing about a ton (which is the normal weight of a V-2 payload). And imagine that our little V-2—let's call it V-3!—itself carried a third and still smaller rocket weighing a tenth of a ton. *By itself*, each of these rockets could reach a speed of around 3,500 miles an hour.

This would be a three-stage rocket. It would be launched by starting the motor of the biggest stage, V-2. When it had reached 3,500 m.p.h., the V-2's tanks would be empty, and a small explosive charge would separate the rockets. V-3 would then start firing, and add its quota of 3,500 m.p.h. until 7,000 m.p.h. had been reached. The same thing would then happen again, and the last stage would go on by itself to reach a speed of no less than 7,000+ 3,500, or 10,500, m.p.h.

There's nothing wrong with this idea; as we'll see in the next chapter, it works. But there's one big snag. The last and fastest stage is so small that it can carry hardly any payload, at the most probably only about twenty pounds. And to do this, we had to start with a rocket weighing more than ten tons!

Nevertheless, the step principle is extremely important and, at least as far as we can see at present, there would be no possibility of building spaceships without it.

The other way in which we might make rockets go faster is by using more powerful propellants. The alcohol-and-liquid-oxygen mixture that drove the V-2 is by no means the only possible combination; there are literally thousands of other mixtures that might be used. In fact, almost anything that will burn quickly enough will make some sort of rocket fuel.

Moreover, there are many more powerful combinations than alcohol and liquid oxygen. Hydrogen burns with oxygen to produce considerably more energy. And instead of oxygen, one can use the still more violently reactive gas fluorine.

Why haven't these better mixtures been used? One answer is that they generate so much heat that rocket engineers haven't been able to make motors that will stand it. There are also such problems as cost and difficulty of handling, but these will be overcome in time. Large rockets are still in their infancy, and the whole science is very much where aviation was before the *First* World War. It is only a matter of time before these more powerful fuels can be safely used, thanks to the experiments now in progress (Plate 10).

Even so, there's a limit to the advances we can expect. However powerful our fuels, and however well-designed our motors, we can't hope to do more than double present performances—and that's nothing like good enough for really economical space-flight.

It's at this point that someone always asks the question: "What about atomic power? Look at the energy that's released when an A-bomb goes off! Surely there's enough there to drive spaceships anywhere you please!"

Well, so there is. The *energy* is certainly there all right —as anyone who's seen the films of the Bikini tests will be willing enough to believe. But an enormous explosion is no use to us; we want a steady, controllable push, which is just what the A-bomb doesn't give.

Still, there's good reason to think that, eventually, spaceships will be driven by atomic energy. We've seen that the only way we can create a thrust in the vacuum of space is by throwing something away from the spaceship as rapidly as possible, thus producing a reaction or recoil. We'd get exactly the same recoil whether we used chemical energy or nuclear energy to blast the exhaust gases out of the rocket nozzle.

This at once suggests one way of applying atomic power to rockets. Besides its use in the bomb, nuclear energy can be liberated at any desired rate in the so-called piles which are already being developed for power production. Without going into details of atomic engineering, all we need say here is that these piles or reactors consist of bars of uranium arranged in a kind of grid, and when operating they develop great quantities of heat.

If a gas was forced through one of these uranium piles, it would absorb some of the heat generated, and therefore would try to expand. By leading it to a properly shaped nozzle, we might thus produce a rocket jet.

The idea seems simple, and one day the engineers may overcome the practical difficulties—which are enormous. However, there is still another way of using nuclear energy for spaceships, and this may prove to be a lot easier.

It's a device which has been called an "electric rocket." So far it exists only on paper, but there is no doubt that it would work.

Instead of using heat to make gases expand out of a nozzle, the idea is to do the same thing by electricity. A very small-scale example of this can be found in the familiar cathode-ray tube of the TV set. Here a stream of electrons, moving at a very great speed, is produced by high voltages in the tube. Though electrons are very tiny, they have *some* mass, and so this stream causes a minute recoil, far too small to be detected in the ordinary way. There is no danger that this stream of tiny electrical bullets, as it paints its pictures on the screen, will ever drill a hole through the glass of your TV set.

Yet scientific studies have shown that this principle could be developed, in the special conditions that exist out in space, to obtain useful thrusts for spaceships. The necessary electric fields could be produced by atomic energy, and in this way we may be able to use the power of the atom to take us to the planets.

This seems a good point to stop and sum up the conclusions we've now reached. Here they are:

First, rockets work better in airless space than they do in an atmosphere.

Second, most of the mass of a rocket or spaceship consists of its propellants, which are burnt in a very short time compared with the total time of flight. Once the rocket has reached the necessary speed to make any trip, the motor can be switched off, and it's then only a matter of waiting until the destination is reached.

Third, the speeds needed for even the easiest of interplanetary voyages are very large, as it takes 25,000 m.p.h. merely to escape from the gravity pull of Earth.

Fourth, such high speeds can be attained by multiple or step-rockets, though they will have to be very big if they are to carry a useful payload.

Fifth, we will eventually have motors and propellants a good deal better than those of today, and sooner or later atomic energy will be used for spaceships.

Finally—and this is something we *haven't* mentioned yet—we will be able to stop and refuel on our way into space, by the use of artificial satellites or man-made moons circling the Earth beyond the atmosphere. This is a subject so important that it deserves a whole chapter of its own, and we'll come back to it again after we've surveyed the achievements of the rockets that are actually flying today.

4 - Above the Atmosphere

WHEN the Second World War ended in 1945, and the results of German rocket research were revealed, aeronautics made a great leap forward—and the new science of *astronautics* was born. For the first time it had become possible to send objects beyond the atmosphere, as the V-2, with its ceiling of 115 miles, was just able to reach space itself.

What, however, do we mean by "space"? As we go higher and higher in the atmosphere, the air gets rapidly thinner—but there is no point at which one can say that it actually ends. Twenty miles up, it's a hundred times thinner than at sea level. That is still quite dense enough to have a considerable effect on bodies moving at high speeds. But a hundred and twenty miles up, the air is less than *one hundred-millionth* of its sea-level density. To get some idea of what this means, imagine that you let a thimbleful of ordinary air expand into a vacuum until it took up as much volume as the average house. The resulting gas would be about as dense as the atmosphere one hundred and twenty miles up! For all practical purposes, therefore, we can say that at such heights we are "in space."

After the fall of Germany the Allies captured many of the giant V-2 rockets and promptly put them to work exploring the upper atmosphere (Plate 11). The great center of this research has been the famous White Sands Proving Ground, in New Mexico. Here the American Army has built a huge experimental base where rockets of all kinds can be tested and fired. The Proving Ground is in uninhabited desert country, and the rockets can travel for a hundred miles or more with no danger of hitting anything except cacti and rattlesnakes.

Since 1946, many hundreds of "shoots" have taken place at White Sands. During the early days, it was not possible to recover the instruments carried in the rocket, and so radio techniques or "telemetering" had to be developed. Each rocket carried a number of low-powered radio transmitters, which automatically sent back to ground stations the readings of the instruments carried on the flight.

In addition, the rockets were tracked by radar and, when the sky was clear, by large telescopes. Thus, the exact position of the missile at every moment of the flight could be determined and matched with the information radioed back by its many instruments.

Very often, things did not go according to plan. Quite a number of the giant rockets exploded soon after take-off, and one veered over horizontally and flew above the heads of the spectators before it crashed into the desert.

From the successful flights, information about the temperature and pressure in the upper atmosphere was obtained, as well as valuable data concerning the mysteri-out cosmic rays which continually bombard us from space. In addition, of course, this work provided valuable training in the many problems connected with handling large rockets.

In the normal way, when a V-2 crashes at the end of its flight it leaves a crater about 30 feet deep, as its impact velocity is about 2,000 miles an hour. However, the American scientists found that if they used small explosive charges to blow off the rocket's nose during its fall back to earth, the streamlining was spoiled and the two parts of the missile landed in recognizable condition. By this rather crude means, they were able to recover photographic and other records carried in specially armored cases.

It is only recently that the obvious solution—landing the instruments by parachute—has been successful. At the enormous velocities involved, ordinary parachutes are useless and special ones have had to be developed.

The giant V-2 was not a very efficient vehicle for research, and in any case supplies of them were limited. So the Americans quickly went to work to develop rockets of their own, and some of these have already beaten the V-2's record height of 115 miles. The most ambitious American research rocket at present is the 5-ton Martin *Viking* (Plate 12), which has reached a height of 158 miles and will eventually go much higher. One of the interesting things about this rocket is the method of control used. As mentioned on page 19 *Viking* steers itself by moving the motor and hence the jet. In films showing the take-off of this rocket, it is fascinating to watch the jet swinging back and forth as it automatically corrects the path of the climbing missile.

The V-2 and the *Viking* are of course single-stage

rockets, but two-step missiles have also been launched and the present records for height and speed are held by such a rocket. In 1949 a V-2 took off carrying a small American rocket known as *WAC Corporal* (Plate 13), and, when the lower stage had exhausted its propellants, the little missile went on by itself to reach a height of 242 miles and a speed of 5,100 m.p.h. The useful payload carried on this trip was very small, but it was an extremely important experiment as it pointed the way to future developments.

Some of the most interesting recent work has involved the first flights of animals into space. After a number of unsuccessful experiments, mice and monkeys were brought back safely to earth from altitudes of forty miles. None of the animals was any the worse for the experience, and films were made of the mice while they were floating around inside their chamber during the period of weight-lessness which, as we will see in the next chapter, is the normal condition in space-flight (Plate 14).

Building rockets which can carry mice or monkeys is obviously much easier than making rockets which can carry men. So far, no manned *pure* rockets have been launched, but a number of flights have been made in rocket-propelled aircraft to very great altitudes, and at speeds which would have seemed fantastic only a few years ago. Unfortunately, as in most of this work, military security has prevented much release of information, and only a few figures have been revealed. But it is known that the Douglas *Skyrocket* (Plate 15) has reached speeds of around 1,300 miles an hour and altitudes of 15 miles, while the Bell X-2, before crashing, climbed 24 miles high

and attained 1,900 miles an hour. In order to conserve
fuel, since rocket motors burn their propellants at a ter-
rific rate, these experimental aircraft have usually been
carried up to the lower stratosphere by bombers, and then
released to begin their own flights. Another application,
one might almost say, of the step principle!

The pilot of an aircraft like the *Skyrocket* must have
many of the experiences that a spaceship pilot will know,
though on a smaller scale and for a few minutes only.
There is the powerful acceleration as the rocket motor
opens up and presses him back in his seat. The Earth
falls behind as he aims the needle-nose of his craft up into
the sky. Then, when he has reached maximum speed and
has no more fuel, the thrust of the rockets vanishes and
for a short time, as the aircraft still continues to climb
under its momentum, he is almost weightless. If he were
not strapped in, he would float around in the cockpit.
Presently, however, the ship loses its speed and begins to
fall back to the denser atmosphere, until at last its wings
grip the air again. Then the pilot has to turn towards home
and land his little craft as a glider.

Many of the problems that will have to be met in spaceship design are already being tackled in the construction
of vehicles such as this. The pilot has to be provided with
air, since, as far as breathing the surrounding atmosphere
is concerned, he might just as well be out in space. The
cockpit also has to be protected against the high temperatures produced by friction as the vehicle hurtles through
the air. Indeed, in many respects it would not be unfair to
say that the *Skyrocket* and its successors are the first short-
range spaceships.

Today, therefore, we have two simultaneous attacks on space in progress. On the one hand, the pure missiles, carrying instrument loads of a few hundred pounds, have climbed to the very limits of the atmosphere—and in some cases far beyond. They are not yet large (or reliable!) enough to carry men, but that will undoubtedly be the next development.

At the same time, rocket aircraft of very high performance are taking men to heights which, before long, should be in the region of forty or fifty miles. These flights will teach us much of the know-how—the practical knowledge—that has to be acquired before true space-travel is possible. And as men go higher, the smaller instrument-carrying missiles will go ahead of them, probing and testing and radioing back their reports.

For space-flight will not be the adventure into the unknown that is often imagined. It will be a step-by-step process; one must learn to walk before one can run. The Wright brothers didn't attempt to build a transatlantic airliner when they started their experiments on flying— and astronautics won't begin right away with someone trying to make a ship that can fly to the Moon.

After the high-speed, high-altitude rockets, the next important step is the rocket that can go around the world. For that opens up new and tremendous possibilities, and brings us into the realm of space-stations—permanent artificial bases circling the Earth beyond the atmosphere. Such bases may not be built for another fifty years, but before that we shall use world-circling rockets in an operation that is really the key to the whole problem of space-flight—*refueling in space.*

5 - On the Frontier of Space

MOST of the things we see in our daily life we take for granted and never give them any thought. Consider the Moon, for example, as it hangs there in the sky on a brilliant, clear night. How many people bother to ask themselves what keeps it up?

There are planets that have no moon at all. If someone from such a world came to Earth, he might be very surprised to see the great silver disc of our satellite floating overhead, and if he knew no astronomy he might well wonder what prevented it from falling down.

The answer to this question, which is of fundamental importance in space-flight, was discovered some three hundred years ago by the great scientist Sir Isaac Newton. The Moon is kept securely in its place by the same force that holds us to the Earth: gravity.

There is a common impression that at a certain height gravity disappears. That's quite untrue; Earth's gravity reaches to the remotest stars. But it gets steadily weaker with distance, and when one is a few million miles away it is so feeble that, for almost all practical purposes, it can be ignored.

Newton's law of gravitation, like most great discoveries, can be put into very simple words. It states that, as one goes away from the Earth, gravity decreases according to the square of one's distance from Earth's center. In other words, doubling your distance reduces the force of gravity to a *quarter*; increasing it tenfold reduces gravity to a *hundredth*.

When we talk of gravity, we ordinarily think of the force that holds us to this Earth. But every planet—every body in the universe, in fact—has a gravity of its own. Its value on any world depends on the size and mass of that world. The giant planet Jupiter has almost three times as powerful a gravity as Earth's; the Moon's gravity, on the other hand, is only a sixth of ours.

Now let us return to the problem: "What keeps the Moon up?"

The mutual gravity of Earth and Moon draws the two bodies together with a force of millions of tons. If it had no movement around the Earth, the Moon would soon crash into us.

But the Moon *has* such a movement, and that is why it doesn't fall down. It's swinging round the Earth in a great circle, moving at a speed of over 2,000 m.p.h. As long as it maintains that speed (and, since there's no air resistance in space, it can't lose it) it can never fall down.

Everyone knows that if you tie a stone at the end of a piece of string, you can set it whirling in a circle with very little effort. This is a crude working model of what happens with the Moon. Here, the pull of gravity plays the same role as the tension of the string.

To sum up, then, the Moon's velocity saves it from falling down, and Earth's gravity prevents it from flying off into space.

It may sound rather a delicate juggling feat, but it isn't anything of the sort. If for any reason the Moon altered its distance slightly, the speed would automatically adjust itself, so there's no danger of anything suddenly going wrong. Indeed, such variations are continually taking place, because the Moon's orbit is not exactly circular.

Now, there is no reason at all why the Moon should be at the particular distance it is. It could be much closer, or much further away—as long as its speed was correctly adjusted to balance gravity at that point. To return to our stone-and-string analogy, we know that the shorter the string, the faster the stone has to be moved. The same rule applies to moons revolving round planets, and to planets revolving round the Sun. Mercury, the nearest planet to the Sun, rushes along at thirty miles a second, whereas remote Pluto, at the borders of the solar system, needs only a tenth of this speed to maintain itself in its orbit. Some planets have at least a dozen moons scattered at all sorts of distances and revolving quite happily in their various orbits. There is no law of nature stopping us from having a moon only a couple of hundred miles up, instead of a quarter of a million miles away.

Such a moon would have to move almost ten times as quickly as the real Moon does, since gravity is much stronger so close to the Earth. But if it were given the correct speed—about 18,000 miles an hour—it would continue to circle our world forever, taking only an hour and a half to complete one revolution.

This, of course, is the principle behind the artificial satellites now being developed for research on the frontiers of space. The important thing to realize is that once we give an object a speed of 18,000 miles an hour just above the atmosphere, it will remain up in space forever and will never fall down again. It won't need any fuel to maintain it there—after all, the Moon has no rocket motors! In fact, a considerable amount of work would have to be done *to bring it down again,* since it could return to Earth only if its speed were neutralized in some way.

Now let's see how this idea can be used to take us along the road to the planets.

Eighteen thousand miles an hour is a tremendous speed, and it cannot be attained by a single-stage rocket. With present fuels and motors, we have to use a three-step rocket to obtain the speed necessary to reach an orbit; we must start with a rocket weighing over ten tons to get a mere twenty pound satellite into space. However, as our engineering knowledge advances, it may be possible to establish an orbit round the Earth with a two-step rocket instead of a three-step one; it will still be difficult and expensive, but not as fantastically expensive as it is today.

The next stage will be for man-carrying rockets to get into an orbit. The vehicles that do this will probably look not unlike the present *Skyrocket*—but they will be the upper steps of giant rockets very much bigger than themselves. These rockets will be launched over the sea so that the empty stages, as they fall back to Earth, will not drop on inhabited territory. They will probably descend by parachute and be towed back to land so that they can be used again.

So now we have our little spaceship, its fuel tanks almost exhausted, spinning around the Earth like a tiny Moon. It would be a fascinating experience, watching the whole world turn beneath you in only ninety minutes. But we're not interested in traveling all this way merely to look at the scenery!

Let's suppose that a second rocket—a "tanker" carrying fuel—were to take off from Earth and fly up into the same orbit. When it turned off its motors, it too would be circling the Earth in just the same way as the first vehicle. They would both be moving in the same direction and at the same speed—18,000 miles an hour. *They would, therefore, be at rest with respect to each other.* (Plate 16.) If they could be connected together by pipe line, it would be possible to transfer fuel from one rocket to the other. In this way, the tanks of the first ship could be replenished. It might be necessary for the tanker rocket to make a number of trips up from the ground before the job could be completed; alternatively, several tankers could be employed. In any case, there would be no great hurry, since the spaceships will go on circling Earth happily as long as we want them to, in exactly the same orbit.

The whole operation is just like refueling in the air, which has been successfully carried out for many years. In some ways, it would be simpler. Out in space, there would be no air resistance to buffet the vehicles and their connecting pipes. Indeed, as they swept silently around Earth, there would be no sense of motion at all. And, still more important, the spaceships and everything in them would be weightless, which would greatly simplify the transfer of fuel and stores.

This business of weightlessness is one that very few people seem to understand. It would be the normal condition in space, but this has nothing to with being "beyond the pull of Earth's gravity." Indeed, as we have already seen, that pull is still powerful hundreds of thousands of miles away. Just above the atmosphere, where our orbital spaceships will be circling, it is practically as strong as it is down here at the surface. Then why should things become weightless?

To answer that question, let's consider what we mean by weight. You feel a sensation of weight only when some force is pressing on you. When you stand, there is the pressure of the ground; when you sit, that of your chair. If the chair or the ground were abruptly removed, you'd feel weightless as long as you remained unsupported. Of course, you'd promptly start to fall, so the condition would last only for a very short time and would terminate painfully.

Now suppose your chair were suddenly to start moving *upwards,* as if in a high-speed elevator. Then you would feel a *greater* weight than normal, as long as the acceleration lasted. This is what we mean when we say that a pilot is "under several gravities": he is in an airplane accelerating so swiftly that his seat presses against him with several times the normal force. And that is what would happen in a spaceship building up speed.

However, as soon as the rocket motors of the spaceship were shut off, this pressure would cease. It would not matter whether the ship were near the Earth, where gravity is intense, or far out in space, where there is virtually no gravity. As soon as the rockets stopped pushing the ship, the ship would stop pushing on the people inside it—and they would float around freely and "weightlessly." This could happen inside a spaceship a few miles up as easily as in one a billion miles from Earth. As soon as the rocket motors were switched on again, "weight" would return. How strong the feeling of weight would be would depend *entirely* upon the rate at which the rockets were accelerating the ship.

Incidentally, do not make the mistake of confusing weight with air pressure—they are two completely different things. The air around us presses on our bodies equally in all directions. Its effect, therefore, cancels out so that we don't feel it, and it contributes nothing to our sensation of weight. This is just as well, as the total air pressure on the human body, under normal atmospheric conditions, is about fifteen tons!

Notice, therefore, that there are really two kinds of "weight." The first is the normal kind, due to gravity. This, of course, would vary from planet to planet. A man who weighed 180 pounds here would weigh only 30 on the Moon—but 480 on Jupiter.

The other kind of weight is that due to acceleration, and is the only kind that can occur aboard a spaceship in flight.

Weightlessness is, therefore, the normal condition for almost the whole duration of any space voyage, for the rockets would operate for only a few minutes at the beginning and end of the trip. No one is quite sure at present just what effect this will have on space-travelers, and unfortunately we cannot carry out any tests down here on Earth. The experiments with mice and monkeys mentioned in the last chapter are encouraging, and there is no reason to suppose that weightlessness will be dangerous. In many ways it will be very useful, since it will enable men to handle great loads with little trouble—and it should really be rather good fun floating about and being able to fly like a bird!

Moving around, however, would present some problems. Walking would be impossible if you had no weight. Inside a spaceship, you could get from one point to another by moving hand-over-hand along the wall, which would certainly be provided with plenty of handholds. A more exciting, but perhaps more dangerous, way of getting around would be to kick-off against one wall and so launch yourself through the air. You would then continue to move in a straight line until you hit something—preferably not with your head!

Outside the spaceship, when you were floating in nothingness with no physical contact with any other object, the only way you could move around would be by means of the rocket principle. You would have to carry a kind of gun which would shoot you along by its recoil. A cylinder of compressed gas would be equally effective, since the escaping gas would act as a sort of cold rocket. A famous sequence in the film *Destination Moon* demonstrated this very well.

Of course, if you were outside the ship in this way, you would have to be wearing a spacesuit. It is quite impossible for an unprotected human being to live for more than a few seconds above the atmosphere. He would not only suffocate owing to lack of oxygen, but the pressure inside his body, no longer balanced by a pressure outside, would cause internal damage.

Spacesuits will be rather complicated pieces of equipment, since they must do many other things as well as provide oxygen. They must be flexible, so that their occupants can move their limbs and won't be spread-eagled by the internal pressure. (If you've ever blown up one of those toy balloons shaped like animals, you'll understand how air pressure can make an object rigid.) Because sound cannot be transmitted unless there is some substance—gas, solid, or liquid—to carry it, space is utterly silent and all communication outside the ship would have to be by radio. The present-day walkie-talkie would not need much improvement to make it very suitable for spacesuits.

Another problem that has to be met in space is that of temperature control. Space itself—being nothing—can, of course, have no temperature. But an object floating in space will have a temperature which depends very largely on the heat it picks up from the Sun. In general, one would be much more likely to get too hot rather than too cold, owing to the intense rays of the Sun, and the popular idea that it is cold in space is completely false.

Even if there were no Sun, a man's body generates enough heat to kill him in a few minutes if it cannot escape. Our spacesuits will, therefore, have to be provided with some automatic means of varying the temperature inside them, and this might be done by a small refrigeration unit.

Many pictures and films have shown spacesuits as having clear, goldfish-bowl helmets completely surrounding the head of the wearer (Plate 17). This may look very pretty, but we can be sure that things won't be quite that way in practice. Out in space, the blinding glare of the Sun, reflected from any object in the field of view, would make it essential for the helmets to be of darkened glass, perhaps with some additional filters or sunshields that could be brought into use at will. Our atmosphere protects us from, among other things, a fierce bombardment of ultraviolet rays from the Sun. The helmet of the suit would have to cut these out completely, otherwise the wearer would be very badly burned in a matter of minutes.

These problems may sound formidable, but they will all be overcome. Many of them have already been tackled, on a small scale, in connection with our present rocket-flights in the upper atmosphere (Plate 18). By the time we are ready to venture out into space for any length of time, we will know a good deal more about the new science of "space medicine" and will be able to provide proper protection for our crews.

By now, you will have appreciated the importance of the satellite rocket. Before we send men up into the orbit around the Earth, we'll have had many automatic missiles up there, teaching us about conditions in space and radioing back their findings. Then the first spaceships will climb into the orbit, using up nearly all their fuel to do so. The tanker rockets will "home" on to them, and men in spacesuits will connect ship and tanker by pipeline, until at last the spaceship is ready to continue on its voyage to the Moon or the planets.

At this point, someone may say, "Surely it's not worthwhile stopping to refuel after two hundred miles, on a journey of millions!" It's a fair question, and the answer shows once again how greatly space-flight differs from transport on the Earth.

We've already mentioned that, if a rocket is to escape from the Earth and never come back, it must reach a speed of 25,000 miles an hour. The circling spaceship, 200 miles up, is already moving at 18,000 miles an hour—nearly three quarters of this speed. *An extra 7,000 miles an hour is therefore all that is required.* The fact that the ship is only 200 miles away doesn't matter. Once it's reached escape velocity Earth can never hold it back and it will coast on out into space.

Spaceships returning to Earth may also go into these orbits, instead of attempting to land directly. They will be met in space by small "ferry" rockets, to which their crews will be transferred for the trip down to Earth. The big spaceships will be left circling above the atmosphere until they are refueled and ready for their next mission.

The great advantage of this is that the short climb through the atmosphere and the long trip across space really require two entirely different sorts of spaceship, and it's very inefficient trying to make one vehicle do the entire trip. It would be like trying to combine the characteristics of bulldozer and racing car. So we will see two kinds of spaceship being developed. The first will be the carefully streamlined, winged vehicle which will leave Earth and climb into the orbit above the atmosphere with its load of fuel and stores for the *real* spaceships already waiting out there. These will not be streamlined at all, and may look very odd objects indeed—perhaps collections of spheres and cylinders held together with struts.

So far we've considered how our spaceships will get into the orbit around the Earth, but we haven't stopped to see how they will get safely back again. Unless they lose their speed, they can't fall down, so one way of making them return would be to employ rocket *braking*—in other words, firing the rockets against the direction of the spaceship's motion.

That would work all right, but it would be extremely expensive in terms of fuel if we had to get rid of all the spaceship's velocity by this means. We would have to carry up a considerable amount of fuel just to make the return journey, and to lift *that* would require a far huger quantity of fuel at the take-off. Fortunately, there is another way.

By using quite a small amount of rocket braking—cutting its speed from 18,000 to, say, 16,000 miles an hour—the spaceship would swing closer to the Earth and would pass through the upper layers of the atmosphere. This would make it lose still more speed owing to air resistance, until before long it would be impossible for it to remain out in space. It would race through the upper air, fifty miles above the Earth, and circle the world several times as a supersonic glider before it came down into the lower atmosphere and landed at no greater speed than an ordinary aircraft. All its original velocity would have been whittled away by air resistance, and it would have become very hot in the process. However, if special heat-resisting materials were used for the parts of the wings and fuselage most affected, the maneuver could be carried out safely without the ship melting down like a meteor.

This scheme of landing by means of air resistance is very important, as it means huge savings of fuel. It could be used not only on Earth but also on planets like Mars and Venus which, as we will see later, have atmospheres. However, it would be of no use at all on the airless Moon, and there we will be forced to rely entirely on our rockets in order to slow down for the landing.

Even now, we have merely begun to describe some of the possibilities raised by these orbits around the Earth. The most spectacular prospects—and the ones which have lately attracted the most attention—are concerned with the building of permanent bases or space-stations beyond the atmosphere. This may not happen until many years after space-flight has begun, but sooner or later it is inevitable. So, before we go further afield and start exploring the planets, let's take a look at these islands in the sky that, a hundred years from now, may be spinning around the world like dozens of tiny moons.

6 - Citizens of Space

WE HERE at the middle of the twentieth century, looking up at the ocean of space, can hardly begin to guess at the things that men may be doing out there a hundred years from now. But we can be fairly sure that there will be many scientists floating on space-stations a few thousand miles above the Earth, studying not only the stars around them but also the planet looming beneath.

Why go outside Earth to study it? Anyone who has ever flown in an airplane should be able to answer that question. One of the most important uses of space-stations will be for weather research. Even at the fairly modest heights so far reached by rockets, wonderful pictures of cloud movements over the surface of the Earth have been obtained (Plate 19). A single station a few thousand miles up could watch the weather over the entire globe in the course of a few hours, as it circled the planet.

For this sort of work, it would be no use having our observers just above the atmosphere: their view of Earth would be limited to too narrow a strip. The "Met Stations" would have to be at least four thousand miles up if the scientists wanted to have a really comprehensive view. At this height, the station would take about four hours to make one circuit of the Earth, as it would be moving in a much wider circle than a satellite just above the atmosphere which needs only ninety minutes for the round trip. It would also be traveling a good deal more slowly, for gravity four thousand miles up is only a quarter of its value down here, and the centrifugal force needed to counteract it is thus reduced.

The astronomers are the scientists looking forward most eagerly to having observatories in space. Even on what seems to be a clear night, when the stars are shining brilliantly, only a small part of the light coming from space actually gets through our atmosphere. And what *does* get through is distorted so that the pictures it carries are never clear. If you look at one of the planets—say Mars —through a powerful telescope, you will find that the image is continually quivering and you can never get a steady view.

Above the atmosphere, all this would be different. Visibility would always be more perfect than anything we can imagine down here on Earth. There would never be night or day; the stars would always be shining, right up to the blazing edge of the Sun! No wonder, then, that astronomers believe their science will make tremendous steps forward when they can carry their telescopes out into space. Climbing the hundred miles that will take us clear of the atmosphere may enable us to solve the mystery of Mars, long before we make the 35,000,000-mile trip to the planet itself.

There have been many suggestions that space-stations

could have military uses, and certainly the Germans during the War, and the United States government after it, have been interested in this idea. If you could watch the weather, you could also watch troop movements, see what battleships and air fleets were doing, and carry out a complete reconnaissance of hostile territory—clouds permitting, of course.

For this reason, it is possible that the military will foot the bill for the first space-stations, but in the long run their peaceful uses will be far more important. One of these uses may eventually affect almost every home in the world.

A space-station would be an ideal site for TV and radio transmitters. The short waves used in TV will not go round the curve of the Earth, which is why our present stations have such a limited range and we have to use enormously expensive coaxial cables or relays if we want to send TV over great distances. But a station up in space, looking down on an entire hemisphere, could broadcast its programs to half the planet at one time. Of course, programs from the Earth's surface would be beamed up to the space-stations, and relayed from there. Two or three such stations could provide complete coverage for the whole Earth (Figure 2).

It would be inconvenient for the customers if they had to keep their TV antennas moving continuously to follow the space-station transmitters as they traveled across the sky. Fortunately, there is a very neat solution to this problem. At a certain distance from the Earth, which happens to be 22,000 miles, it would take just one day for a satellite to make its complete circuit. But the Earth, of course, also takes one day to turn on its axis. This means that, from our point of view, the satellite would be always fixed in the sky—it would never rise nor set.

At first sight, this seems a very extraordinary situation, but something nearly like it happens in the case of one of Mars's little moons. The "radio-satellite," when we build it, would be much too far away to be seen by the naked

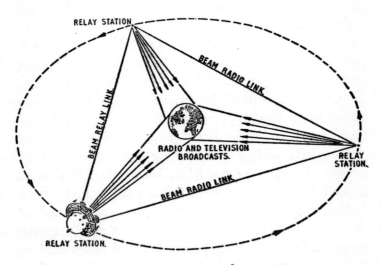

Fig. 2.   Space-station relay system.

eye, but it would be a simple matter to swing one's TV antenna round the sky until the signal came in strong and clear. Then it could be fixed in this position, and it need never be moved again.

A chain of relay stations around the Earth could do much more than provide world-wide TV. It would also make possible a far more efficient radio service than any that exists today, and would cut out most of the inter-ference and distortion that arises when we attempt long-distance communication. Eventually, relays in space should enable us to have a perfect world telephone system, in which anyone anywhere on Earth could dial a number and speak with perfect clarity to anybody else.

Perhaps the most startling idea, though it is not so fantastic as it may seem at first, is that space-stations may one day be used for hospitals and medical research. Their advantages for this purpose arise from the weightless condition that would exist in them. Many kinds of muscular and heart disease could be treated more readily when the patient's weakened body had much less work to do, owing to the absence of weight. The continuous and brilliant sunlight, suitably filtered, of course, would also help convalescence, and the wonderful view of the slowly turning Earth would provide an unending spectacle.

These are only some of the possible uses of space-stations, and it is also certain that they would be of enormous value for many forms of scientific research. When space-travel is as fully established as air transport is today, some of these stations may become veritable space-ports where the interplanetary liners and the short-range ferry rockets from Earth meet to exchange passengers and cargo. There seems no limit to the ultimate possibilities, and perhaps one day there may be millions of people living in space-cities and looking down with scorn upon the inhabitants of Earth exhausting themselves, and perhaps shortening their lives, in their endless struggle against gravity.

But let us return from the far future and consider how such stations in space might be built, and what they would look like. Clearly, they could not be constructed on Earth and carried up in any rocket, however big. They would have to be assembled in space from prefabricated parts.

Suppose the design, and the most suitable orbit, have been decided upon. Take a figure we have already mentioned—a height of four thousand miles. To stay in this orbit, a satellite would have to move at about 12,000 miles an hour, and would take four hours to complete one circuit round the Earth.

It would be a tricky problem, designing the space-station so that all its parts were small enough to go into the cargo hold of a freight-carrying rocket. When the first load of parts was ready, the freighter would climb up into the orbit, and reach the necessary speed of 12,000 miles an hour. Then the hatches would be opened, and the cargo would be quite literally dumped in space. A low-powered radio beacon would probably be attached to it so that it could be found without difficulty on later trips.

When the freighter returned to Earth for its next load, it would leave behind a miscellaneous collection of boxes and girders, tied together with light ropes to prevent them drifting apart. They would go on revolving round the world with clockwork precision, so that astronomers could tell within a few miles where they would be a thousand years later. There would be no danger of anything happening to them; in empty space, the girders could not rust!

Eventually, after many trips by the freighter rockets, all the bits and pieces would have been gathered together in the orbit. Then the construction crews would have to start work.

Wearing spacesuits, they would be working under some difficulties, but they would also have several great advantages. Most important of all, nothing would have any weight. The largest girder, given a gentle push, would start to move slowly *and would continue to move* until brought to rest again. Much of the work of assembly could be done by hauling on ropes, but recoil pistols or gas cylinders would also have to be used a good deal for propulsion.

The complete absence of "up" or "down" would at first be very confusing, but the human brain is incredibly adaptable and the workmen would soon come to take their "space acrobatics" for granted. They would be reassured, also, by the fact that they could step back and look at their work with no danger of falling—which they certainly could not do if they were building skyscrapers down on Earth!

A great many designs for space-stations have been put forward by students of the subject (Plates 20 and 21), but most of them have several features in common. First of all, of course, the station must be airtight so that the men inside it don't have to wear spacesuits all the time. Its temperature must also be controlled, and, in fact, it would have to have all the gadgets necessary on a space-ship, apart from the rocket motors themselves. Indeed, it might even be fitted with very low-powered rockets, so that it could make any minor adjustments to its orbit that proved necessary.

Most designers of space-stations have proposed the use of large mirrors to collect sunlight and thus provide power. Out in space, in direct sunlight, almost two horsepower of heat energy falls on every square yard—and when you realize how far away from the Sun we are, that gives you some faint idea of its total horsepower. Two horsepower per square yard over the entire surface of a sphere 93,-000,000 miles in radius (that is, a sphere embracing the Earth's orbit) is an impressive figure! It seems a pity to waste this energy, and it could easily be collected by suitable mirrors and used to run some kind of turbine, thus producing the electricity needed in the station.

Another popular idea is to have space-stations disk- or wheel-shaped, and slowly revolving. By this means, it would be possible to have a kind of artificial gravity inside, because centrifugal force would come into play. The people inside the station would be pressed against the rim of the wheel, and the resulting sensation of weight would be exactly like the real thing. The effect would get smaller as one went towards the center, and at the middle of the wheel there would be no "weight" at all.

The spin would be quite slow, as only a small amount of artificial gravity would be needed, just enough to enable one to walk about in the normal way, and to prevent objects drifting about in the air as they would if there were no weight at all (Figure 3).

The space-station would be set spinning in the first place by attaching small rockets to its rim and firing them for a calculated period of time. After that it would keep on revolving forever, just as the Earth does, because there would be no friction to slow it down.

This spin would, however, introduce complications when one tried to get aboard the station: it would be rather like climbing on a merry-go-round in full swing, for the rim of a really large space-station might be moving around at thirty miles an hour. Perhaps the best way to

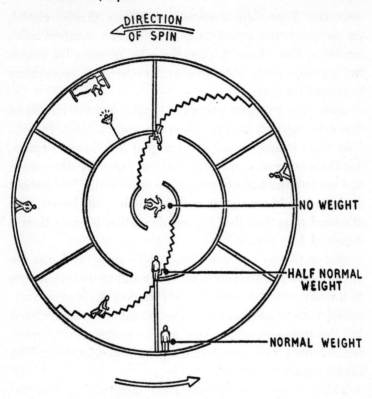

Fig. 3. Gravity in the space-station.

see how one might get over this difficulty is to imagine that we are in a rocket that has climbed up from Earth and is now approaching the station.

As you look through the observation windows of the rocket, you first catch sight of the station as a brilliant light slowly flashing in the distance. This puzzles you for a moment, until you realize that what you are seeing is sunlight reflected from the metal surfaces as the station revolves. Your ship is approaching very slowly, closing in on the station at not much more than a hundred miles an hour. From time to time the pilot corrects his course with gentle bursts of the rockets, producing a momentary return of weight.

Now you are close enough to make out the details of the extraordinary structure you are approaching. It looks like some strange metal toy hanging out there in space, for there is no way in which you can judge its size—there are no familiar objects around to give scale. You almost feel you could reach out and take it in your hands, and it's hard to realize that the whole station is more than a hundred feet across.

Not until you are less than a mile away, and can see such details as observation windows and radio aerials, can you really judge its true size. It's shaped like a giant cartwheel with four spokes, and the resemblance is increased by the presence of an axle at the center. Using mere fizzles from his steering jets, the pilot is cautiously making his way towards this axle.

That's funny—the space-station is revolving, but the axle isn't! Now you understand how you are going to go aboard. The axis of the station is really a hollow tube, not rigidly fixed to the station which is thus "free-wheeling" round it. So it's safe for your spaceship and the axle to be connected together.

There's a soft thump as contact is made, inflated bumpers taking up the shock of impact. Men in spacesuits have emerged from the station and are connecting cables to your ship. Presently there are various clangings and scratchings from the airlock, and a steady hissing (which is highly disconcerting at first!) as pressure equalizes. Then the airlock doors open, and you're free to go into the station.

You're still weightless, of course, as you float through the hollow tube, and at its end you emerge into a big, drum-shaped chamber. It's very slowly turning around

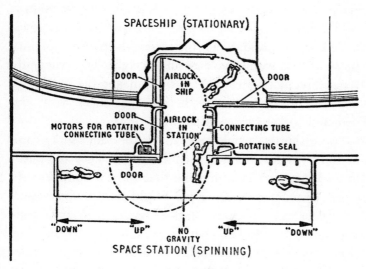

Fig. 4. Going aboard the space-station.

you, and men appear to be standing on the walls, looking up at you. There are some hand-holds conveniently placed where you can grip them as they move slowly past, and with the slightest of jerks you take up the spin of the station. It's really no more difficult than stepping onto a moving escalator (Figure 4). As you start to move you feel weight again. At first it's very slight, perhaps not more than ten pounds, but it will increase as you go outwards towards the more rapidly moving rim of the station.

Not all space-stations may be given spin, for in some cases it might be desirable to be completely weightless. The astronomers, with their big telescopes, would also find it highly inconvenient if their observatories turned completely around every ten seconds or so. In cases like these, two stations might be built within a few miles of each other. One would be the living quarters, and would be spinning so that, when they were sleeping or off duty, the scientists would have normal weight. The other—the space-laboratory—would have no spin, and the staff would move across from one to the other in small, very low-powered rocket ferries or shuttles.

These shuttles would play much the same sort of role in space as the familiar jeep has done here on Earth. Indeed, one can well imagine that they would be christened "space-jeeps"! Their job would be to move objects around outside the space-stations, or to make trips from one station to another. They would have no streamlining, of course, and would probably be little more than stubby cylinders with a small rocket motor at one end. A top speed of a few hundred miles an hour is all that they would need for most purposes, and because of their low power it might take them several minutes to reach this. They could then coast, if needs be, for thousands of miles until they came to their destination and had to use their rockets again to make a safe approach.

There is certainly something about the space-station, floating forever high above the world, that catches the imagination almost as much as the idea of traveling to other planets. The first stations will be very small and very close, perhaps circling only five hundred miles up and carrying half a dozen men in very cramped conditions. It may be a century or more before the ambitious space-cities we have talked about are finally built. Some of these, it is interesting to note, would be visible to the naked eye under favorable conditions. At night one might see them as tiny, swiftly moving stars. And they would have one very peculiar characteristic. The closer stations would rise in the *west* and go backwards across the sky, setting in the *east*—the exact opposite of all the other heavenly bodies!

A little thought will show why this would happen. We see the stars rise in the east because the Earth is turning towards that direction, once every twenty-four hours. But a space-station would move around the world in a few hours—perhaps in as little as ninety minutes—much more quickly, therefore, than the Earth itself turns on its axis. It would thus overtake Earth's rotation and climb up out of the *western* sky.

There's a common example of this sort of thing that everyone has seen. When you are in a train moving at 30 miles an hour and an express passes you at a much greater speed, you seem to be moving backwards. It's an example of what is called relative velocity.

We have seen that, once a station had been given the correct speed for its particular orbit, it could never fall down but would carry on, circling the Earth forever. The only danger that could ever threaten it would be meteors, and, since these seem to scare a lot of people, let's see how much of a menace they really represent.

First of all, what exactly is a meteor? Well, it's a frag-
ment of rock or metal traveling through space—perhaps
part of the general debris left over when the planets were
formed. The total number of meteors in the whole of
space is inconceivably huge, for billions of them hit the
Earth every day. The vast majority are burned up by friction in the atmosphere, and only a very few of the larger
ones reach the ground. Every so often meteors weighing
several pounds, or even tons, fall to Earth, but these are
so rare that in all history there are only a couple of cases
of men having been killed by them.

Above the protecting shield of the atmosphere, however, one might expect to encounter meteors of every size,
and even the tiny ones might be dangerous because of
their tremendous speeds—up to 150,000 miles an hour. At
such velocities, a meteor the size of a pinhead could do
more damage than a rifle bullet. This has made some
people, who have not studied the matter carefully, jump to
the conclusion that spaceships would be promptly riddled
as soon as they left the atmosphere.

Fortunately, although there are so many meteors, there
is a lot more of space, and, when you work out the chances
of being hit by anything large enough to do damage, you
find that spaceships on reasonably short journeys have
nothing to worry about. During the course of a few years,
however, a space-station might expect a few punctures
unless it took suitable precautions. A great deal of protection could be obtained by the simple device of giving
the station a double wall, which would probably be done
in any case for other reasons.

Once in many years, both walls would be penetrated,

more than two or three of them in th
e.

brilliant of the planets keep close to th
may see them in the morning or th
er in the midnight sky. This is becaus
d the Sun well *inside* the orbit of Earth
glare of cities, people sometimes look u
early evening when the Sun has just se
brilliant glare of Venus, hanging like a ti
e sky. It is so brilliant, indeed, that it
see in broad daylight if you know exact

planet inside Earth's orbit is Mercury,
Sun that it is not often noticed, though it
iant object when you can catch it against t

y all move round the Sun in roughly circu
the Sun at the center, the distances betwe
s are continually altering. At its nearest, Ver
00 miles away from Earth and thus comes clo
any other planet. Unfortunately, we can't
it on these occasions, as it is then between
Sun. That means that it is not only lost in
are, but that its dark side is turned toward us.
es Venus and Mercury, there would be three ot
planets visible from time to time. You would of
e to see them high in the southern sky at midnigh
er words, as far away from the Sun as they co
ly get. If you think it over, you'll realize that
s that they must move on paths *outside* the Ear

but even this need not be serious. True, the air would start to rush out, but it would take several minutes before the pressure dropped to a dangerously low value, and there would be plenty of time to seal the leak.

There may be other dangers and problems which will have to be overcome before we can build space-stations; the mysterious cosmic rays, for example, still present an unknown hazard. But unknown dangers often have a habit of disappearing when they are firmly faced, like the imaginary sea monsters that Columbus was undoubtedly warned against when he set sail towards the west.

7 - The Heavens Around Us

THE time has now come for us to look further into space—far beyond the remotest of the satellite space-stations we discussed in the last chapter. We're going to make a quick tour of the universe, to discover something about the places we will be able to visit when we have perfected space-travel, and flight beyond the atmosphere has become an everyday achievement.

When you look up at the sky on a clear night, it seems packed with stars. It is hard to believe—and it was many thousands of years before it was discovered—that all those stars are suns. Most of those that you can see are at least as bright as our own Sun, and some of them are hundreds or thousands of times brighter. Yet they are at such colossal distances that they appear merely as points of light, giving no trace of heat. Almost all are at least a *million* times further away than our Sun—or, to put it in another way, if our Sun were carried off to a million times its present distance, it would be just another star, and a faint one at that.

If all the stars were suddenly wiped out of existence,

it wo
they
probab
be left.

First
Moon. T
everyone
further aw
impossible,
body in the s
and planets m
control the pa
to other worlds
ever going to th
metal could rem
Moreover, its gra
28 times as much t
alone would be eno

Matters are very
much smaller world
away, as compared wi
Nevertheless, the total
that of the whole conti
quite a while to explore
and all the other planets
shines only by the reflecte

Even if we abolished th
would not be the only objects
skies. There would be five o
just like stars but moving in th
the stars never did. These woul

would seldom see
sky at any one tin
Two of the mos
Sun, so that you
evening, but nev
they travel arou
Even amid the
and see, in the
the dazzlingly
arc lamp in tl
quite easy to
where to look
The other
close to the
quite a brill
sunset glow
Since th
paths, witl
the planet
is 26,000,0
to us tha
much of
and the
Sun's g
Besi
bright
be abl
in otl
possi
mea

orbit, unlike Mercury and Venus, so that we can get between them and the Sun.

These three planets are Mars, Jupiter, and Saturn. At their closest to us they are, respectively, 35,000,000 miles, 390,000,000 miles, and 793,000,000 miles away. You will see from these last figures that the inner planets Mercury, Venus, and Earth are quite crowded together as compared with the outer ones.

This list contains all the planets that were known before the invention of the telescope. Together with the Sun and Moon, they would be the only visible objects left in the sky if the stars suddenly disappeared. There are, however, three more planets—Uranus, Neptune, and Pluto— which you would need a telescope to see. They are all further away than Saturn, and the last one of all, Pluto, is 3,675,000,000 miles from the Sun. It is quite likely that there are still other planets beyond Pluto, but they will be extremely faint and hard to discover. So at the moment, Pluto represents the frontier of the Sun's domain.

Picture, then, this little family of worlds, all revolving in the same direction around their giant central Sun. Our own Earth is the third out, counting from the Sun, and it's not a very conspicuous member of the family. True, four of the planets—Mercury, Venus, Mars, and Pluto— are smaller than Earth. However, the other four—Jupiter, Saturn, Uranus, and Neptune—are *very* much bigger.

One of the lessons that astronomy teaches us is that there is nothing very outstanding or unusual about our place in the universe. We've no reason to be ashamed of our planet, but no reason to be conceited about it either!

Most of the planets have satellites, or moons, revolving

round them. Our world, of course, has one, which we call *the* Moon. Mars has two, Jupiter twelve, Saturn nine, Uranus five, Neptune two. Mercury and Venus have none, and Pluto is too far away for us to tell. Most of these moons are very small indeed, and there are probably many others that we have not yet discovered.

All the planets have atmospheres, that is, they are surrounded by layers of gas. Some of these layers are enormously thick and dense, others very thin indeed. Unfortunately, there is not a single planet with an atmosphere which we could breathe, so anything you may have read about people like us living on the other worlds of our own Sun is simply not true. In Chapter 11 we'll have a closer look at conditions on the planets, but we can say right away that there's no other place like Earth, in our solar system at least. This means, of course, that any forms of life we may meet elsewhere will be quite strange. That makes the prospect of interplanetary travel all the more exciting, for it would be rather dull if everywhere we went we discovered that conditions were just the same as here!

Although the distances between the planets seem so enormous by our usual standards, that is not as great a handicap to space-flight as one might think. Between the worlds there is a perfect vacuum, and hence no air resistance at all. Thus a spaceship could not lose any of its original velocity through friction, and under the right conditions could keep up its speed forever, just as the Earth does in its eternal circling of the Sun. So interplanetary flight is largely a question of aiming yourself in the right direction, building up the proper speed—and then sitting back to wait.

The Sun and its planets form what is known as the solar system, and despite its size this system is a very tiny affair when compared with the distances to the other suns—the stars. For example, the *very nearest* star is almost 10,000 times as far away as the remotest planet, Pluto. This means that, when we have explored all the planets, we will be nowhere near conquering the enormously greater distances to the stars. But there would be no point in going to the stars, anyway, unless we were sure that they had planets or solar systems of their own. At the moment, we have no way of discovering this.

However, the eight planets and thirty-one moons should keep us busy for some centuries to come—and at the end of that time, no doubt, men will be speculating about the possibility of inter*stellar* travel in just the same way as we speculate about inter*planetary* travel today.

The first of the other worlds which men will reach and explore will undoubtedly be the Moon, for it is so much closer to us than any other body in space. Even Venus, nearest of the planets, is more than a hundred times further away. Because of its closeness, we also know a great deal more about the Moon than any other world, so our first explorers will not be going completely into the unknown. Let's follow them now on one of those voyages—those great adventures of the future which many of you who are reading these words will live to see . . .

8 - Flight to the Moon

IT'S four minutes to take-off, and you're trying to tell yourself that you aren't *really* afraid. The pilot has finished checking his instruments, and from time to time a voice from the control tower comes through a loudspeaker. Otherwise it is quiet—almost too quiet. To occupy your mind, you examine the masses of instruments and try to decide what they all do. Some of them, the fuel, pressure, and temperature gauges, for example, are obvious, but there are others of which you can't make head or tail. You wonder how anyone can ever learn what they're all for. Just suppose the pilot made a mistake and pressed the wrong button . . .

Suddenly, an electric motor starts to whir close at hand. Then things begin to happen all over the place: switches click, powerful pumps begin to whine, and valves start to snap open down in the heart of the great rocket in whose streamlined nose you are sitting. With each new noise you think, "This is it!"—but still you don't move. When the voyage finally begins, you aren't prepared for it.

A long way off, it seems, there's a noise like a thousand

waterfalls, or a thunderstorm in which the crashes follow each other so quickly that there's no moment of silence between them. The rocket motors have started, but are not yet delivering enough power to lift the ship. Quickly the roar mounts, the cabin begins to vibrate, and the spaceship rises from the face of the desert. Outside, the Arizona sands are being sprayed with flame for a hundred yards around.

Something seems to be pushing you down, quite gently, into the thick padding of your couch. It isn't at all uncomfortable, but the pressure mounts until your limbs seem to be made of lead and it takes a deliberate effort to keep breathing. You try to lift your hand, and the effort needed to move it even a few inches is so tiring that you let it drop back beside you. You lie limp and relaxed, waiting to see what will happen next. You're no longer frightened: it's too exciting for that, this feeling of infinite power sweeping you up into the sky.

There's a sudden fall in the thunder of the rockets, the sensation of immense weight ebbs away, and you can breathe more easily. Power is being reduced; in a few moments, Earth will no longer be able to recapture you. A minute later silence comes flooding back as the motors cut out completely, and all feeling of weight vanishes. For a few minutes the pilot checks his instruments; then he turns round and smiles.

"Nicely on course; we'll make our rendezvous in forty minutes. You can get up if you want to."

Gingerly, you ease yourself out of the couch, holding on to it with one hand. You feel rather like a captive balloon as you float there in space; then you pluck up courage and gently push yourself across the cabin. You float slowly over to the observation port, anxious to have a look at Earth.

You'd expected to see a great globe hanging in space, with the seas and continents clearly visible—just like one of those globes you find in map-sellers' windows, except that there wouldn't be any lines of longitude and latitude. What you *do* see, however, is so unexpected and so wonderful that it takes your breath away. Almost filling the sky is a tremendous, blinding crescent, the shape of a new moon but hundreds of times bigger. The rocket is passing over the night side of Earth, and most of the planet is in darkness. You can see it dimly as a vast, shadowy circle eclipsing the stars. Here and there are patches of phosphorescence—the lights of great cities.

As you wait, the narrow crescent slowly grows until presently you are looking down on the sunlit side of the planet. It's taken you just over forty minutes to travel half-way round the world! Then the pilot tells you to go back to your couch while he "homes" on the spaceship that is already circling up here, waiting for you to go aboard.

It's an ugly-looking machine, nothing like the sleek, streamlined torpedo that carried you up from Earth. In fact, it's a stubby cylinder, rounded at one end and with a shock-absorbing undercarriage at the other. The rounded end is fitted with several windows and a lot of radio equipment, while between the undercarriage legs you can see the jets of rocket nozzles.

This is the Lunar Shuttle, built up here in space in exactly the same way as the space-stations were constructed. Its job is to circle the Earth and take aboard passengers and supplies for the colony on the Moon. Moving in its orbit above the atmosphere at 18,000 miles an hour, it can then build up the extra 7,000 miles an hour that will let it escape from the Earth. Its rocket motors are far too weak to enable it to land on Earth or take off again, but they are powerful enough to fight the Moon's much weaker gravity, so that the Shuttle can make the trip down to the Moon and back again to its orbit around Earth.

It's several hours later, and you're now aboard the Shuttle waiting for the *real* journey to begin. The rocket that carried you up from Earth has returned to its base, having fallen back into the atmosphere and landed as a glider. The first lap of your journey is over; climbing that hundred miles has taken more fuel than the quarter of a million miles that remains.

The Shuttle is quite large, and several passengers are already aboard. They came up, you gather, on earlier ferry flights. Since the journey is going to last several days, there are little bunks in which you can sleep, and there's a tiny lounge in which you can sit and read or look at the stars.

At last everything is ready. The pilot waits for the carefully calculated instant and starts the motors. This time, the force urging you down into your couch is very gentle —hardly enough, in fact, to give you your normal weight. The Shuttle is taking its time to build up speed, to add the extra 7,000 miles an hour that will tear it away from Earth. The vibration of the rockets lasts for many minutes;

then silence falls and your weight vanishes once more. It will not return until you reach the Moon.

Yet everything still seems exactly the same. The Earth hasn't moved, and you still appear to be going around it just as you were before. You'll have to wait for a while if you want to see any change.

An hour later there's no doubt about it. Earth is a good deal smaller; it's slowly falling astern. You're traveling outwards on the long curve which, without any more effort on the part of the rockets, will take you to the Moon . . . (Figure 5).

Space-travel may sound exciting, but I'm afraid you'll be rather bored before the five days of the journey are up. All that will happen is that Earth will slowly shrink astern, while the Moon slowly grows ahead. Since, of course, there is no sensation of motion whatsoever, only logic tells you that you are really approaching the Moon. The nose of the ship isn't pointing anywhere in particular; in fact, as it travels along, the Shuttle very slowly turns end over end. Not until it is time to land will the pilot bother to check the ship's spin.

That time has come at last. For some hours, the gravity field of the Moon has been increasing—and so has the ship's speed. But you can't feel this, since you are still weightless as the ship is in free fall.

The Moon is now only a few hundred miles away, and so enormous that it seems to fill the sky. Indeed, it's no longer a globe hanging in space but a jagged landscape spread out far below. You can see countless mountains and craters, many of whose names you've learned from the maps in the past few days. They're beginning to look much too close for comfort . . .

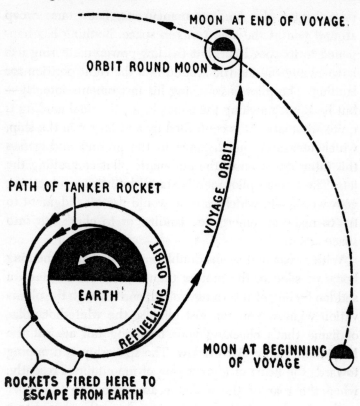

MOON AT END OF VOYAGE.

ORBIT ROUND MOON

PATH OF TANKER ROCKET

VOYAGE ORBIT

REFUELLING ORBIT

EARTH

MOON AT BEGINNING
OF VOYAGE

ROCKETS FIRED HERE TO
ESCAPE FROM EARTH

Fig. 5. The Earth-Moon trip.

The ship is falling at over 5,000 miles an hour towards that inhospitable world. Since there is scarcely a trace of atmosphere, you can't use wings or parachutes to land, and will therefore have to rely entirely on the rockets. That means turning the ship around in space so that the jets—and the elaborate shock-absorbing equipment of the undercarriage—point downwards.

You have strapped yourself in your couch when the

pilot begins the landing maneuvers. The stars sweep around you as the ship turns in space. Nothing has happened to its speed yet, but the low-powered steering jets have swung the Shuttle around into the right position for landing. The pilot is watching his instruments intently— but he is not touching the controls, for the final landing is quite automatic. It is controlled by a radar set in the ship, which measures the distance to the ground and passes this information on to the automatic pilot controlling the jets. The human pilot merely stands by in case something goes wrong—in which case he would use his judgment to try to make an emergency landing or to climb out into space again.

With a roar that seems doubly impressive after the long hours of silence, the motors thunder into life. There's a sudden feeling of returning weight, and through the observation window you can just glimpse the white-hot pillar of flame that's checking your headlong fall against the Moon, still many miles below. The spaceship is dropping towards the heart of a great ring of mountains. Presently, when the roar of the rocket ceases, some of the taller peaks already seem to be towering above the ship. For a few seconds you are falling free once more, and for a horrible moment you wonder if power has failed and you are about to crash on those cruel hills. Then the rockets flare out again, and the scene below vanishes in fire and clouds of dust blasted up by the jet. A moment later there's the gentlest of impacts, then utter silence.

You are on the Moon.

9 - The Moon

THOUGH the Moon may seem small and unimportant compared with the planets, its nearness makes up for this, and the first great interplanetary explorations will take place on its rugged landscape. Even today, thanks to the patient work of many astronomers, we have very good maps of its surface. Tens of thousands of craters have been carefully charted, and about a thousand of them have been given names, mostly after great philosophers or scientists.

Incidentally, few people realize how much you can see of the Moon's surface through a good pair of prismatic binoculars or the sort of telescope that many families have lying around the house. Indeed, you can make a telescope for less than a dollar that will show all the main lunar craters. All you need is a fairly powerful magnifying lens for an eyepiece, and a weak, convex one (a spectacle lens will do) for the main lens. When you've found by trial how far apart they have to be placed to act as a telescope, mount them in a cardboard tube—or even fix them on a piece of board without bothering about a tube.

Such a telescope will give an *upside-down* picture, but don't mind that, so do all astronomical telescopes; and star or Moon maps are drawn accordingly. Before you start observing, though, there are two hints. First, make sure that the telescope is fixed firmly; it's no use holding it in your hand. And second, don't expect to see any lunar craters when the Moon is nearly full. There are no shadows then, and everything looks flat and rather uninteresting. Look at the Moon when it's around *half-full*, and then you'll see all the craters standing out wonderfully along the shadow-line (Plate 22).

At first sight it would seem that looking through a telescope could tell you about the Moon's geography, but couldn't give much idea of what it was actually like there. However, simple observation can tell a great deal. The fact that we never see any clouds on the Moon proves at once that it has no atmosphere, and therefore no life of the type that exists on Earth. And with our modern instruments, we can actually learn such facts as the temperature of the lunar surface. The first explorers will, therefore, have a very good idea of the conditions they will have to face.

Moreover, no landing will be made on the Moon until we have examined its surface from very close quarters by reconnaissance flights carried out by spaceships leaving their orbit around the Earth, circling the Moon while surveying it with cameras and telescopes, and then returning. Before a manned ship lands on the Moon, radio-controlled landings will probably be made by small robot rockets, so that everything can be tested without risk to life.

The absence of an atmosphere is the first and most serious problem that the explorers will have to face. While they are in the spaceship, of course, there will be no trouble, and a great deal could be learned about the Moon even if no one went outside the rocket. It would be possible to carry out many scientific experiments and to collect samples of lunar rocks by means of suitable instruments. The surrounding landscape might even be investigated by small robot tanks sent out from the ship and remotely controlled by radio. They would be fitted with TV and could collect any interesting specimens that their operator came across.

However, no one is going to go to the Moon if he can only sit in a cabin and look out of the window. So space-suits will be taken in which men can live and work for several hours outside the ship. The suits used would be very similar to those we have already described in Chapter 5, but they would have a few additional refinements making them suitable for lunar conditions. As the Moon's gravity is one sixth of Earth's, a suit which was much too heavy to wear here would be no handicap on the Moon.

Apart from the adventure and excitement, why should men want to go to the Moon? Well, first of all there are the scientific reasons. We have never had a chance of examining any world except our own, and almost every branch of science will make great advances when we can carry out experiments, and make investigations, on a totally different world. One of the first things we'll try to discover is the origin of the thousands of craters and circular "walled plains" that cover so much of the Moon's surface (Plate 23). Were they caused, as some astronomers think, by the impact of enormous meteors in the remote past? But if so, why are some areas almost free from them? Or were they, on the other hand, entirely "home-grown"—produced by volcanic forces inside the Moon itself?

Because the Moon may never have had an atmosphere or any seas, its geological history will be quite different from Earth's, and we may well expect to find many new minerals there. The low gravity, and the presence of so many craters, may make the exploration of the Moon's interior a fairly simple task.

Is there life on the Moon? That is a question that is always being asked, and most astronomers would say, "Definitely, no. The absence of air and water rules it out." However, it is wise not to be too dogmatic on this point. Many careful lunar observers have seen changes which they believe are due to some form of vegetation, and, when one considers some of the weird plants that have adapted themselves to life in Earth's desert regions, it does not seem impossible that we might find remote relatives of our cacti or lichens on the Moon. This will certainly be one of the first things that our explorers will investigate.

When several expeditions have landed safely on the Moon and returned to Earth, plans would be made to set up a permanent scientific base there. It would probably be largely underground, to avoid the great variations in temperature between the lunar day and night, which last 27 times as long as ours. (At the surface, there's a difference of about 400 degrees Fahrenheit between noon and midnight! However, a few feet down the temperature hardly varies day or night.)

In many ways, the Moon will be an even better site than a space-station for an astronomical observatory. Visibility will be just as good, and there will be firm anchorage for the largest instruments. The fact that the Moon turns so slowly on its axis—once in 27 *days* as compared with Earth's once in 24 *hours*—will also be a considerable advantage to the astronomers. Even during the lunar day it would be easy to observe the stars, because there is no atmosphere to scatter the sunlight and so to swamp the stars in its glare. With a properly shielded telescope, one could observe the stars right up to the edge of the Sun.

The first lunar base would have to be supplied from Earth, in much the same way as research stations in the Antarctic are provisioned from home. However, as the cost of transport will be so great, it will be necessary to make the base self-supporting at the earliest possible moment.

Since there is no air or water, this idea may seem fantastic, but it's really nothing of the sort. For what is air? The important part is the oxygen, and oxygen is one of the main constituents of most rocks. It makes up no less than *half* the crust of the Earth, and there's no reason to suppose that it will be any rarer on the Moon. Because it will be combined chemically, it will require heat and other means to set it free; but with atomic power, we should have all the energy we need for this sort of operation. Eventually, therefore, the lunar colony will be able to build up its own stocks of the precious gas and will have no need to import any from Earth.

Water must also be present on the Moon, as it is on Earth, combined with various salts and other chemicals in many types of rock. When we have had a chance to do some lunar prospecting (Plate 21), we should be able to locate supplies of any material we need. It would then be possible to grow crops on the Moon in pressurized glasshouses, feeding the growing plants on chemicals produced from the Moon itself. The method of cultivation known as hydroponic or soilless farming would be very suitable for this purpose. In this system, the plants are supported on wire netting and their roots dip into solutions of the necessary salts. Crops can be grown far more rapidly than under normal conditions, and also take up much less space. The fourteen days of continuous sunlight which one would have during the lunar "day" would also make things much easier for the farmer!

Altogether apart from purely scientific reasons, there are extremely powerful practical incentives for the colonization of the Moon. Because of its low gravity, it is more than twenty times easier to escape from the Moon than from the Earth. If we can find sources of rocket propellants there, and thus set up refueling stations on the Moon, the problem of interplanetary flight will be enormously simplified.

Let's jump perhaps a hundred years into the future, to the time when the Moon is no longer the frontier but has been fairly widely explored and settled. You're with a party of other colonists, leaving one of the underground bases on a trip across the surface. Surprisingly enough, you are making the journey in a very old-fashioned form of transport—a bus!

Old-fashioned or not, it's the only reasonable method. Rockets are far too expensive for short distances, and, since there is no atmosphere, normal air transport is out of the question. However, it's not at all an ordinary bus. It's airtight, of course, and is really a sort of mobile hotel in which a dozen people can live comfortably for a week. The whole vehicle is about forty feet long and is mounted on two sets of caterpillar tractors, operated by powerful electric motors. The driver has a little raised cabin at the front, and the passenger compartment is fitted with comfortable seats that become bunks to sleep on. At the back is a kitchen, storeroom, and even a tiny shower bath.

The outer doors of the giant airlock leading into the underground garage have now opened, and you slowly climb up the ramp to the surface. Soon you're rolling briskly across the crater floor at about forty miles an hour. It's easy to make good speed here as the ground is quite level and any obstacles have already been bulldozed out of the way to make the rough track you're following. You hope that there will soon be a change of scenery; it will be rather dull if it's like this all the way.

Your wish is soon granted. Far ahead, a line of jagged peaks has become visible on the horizon, and minute by minute they climb higher in the sky. At first, because of the steep curvature of the Moon's surface, it seems that the bus is approaching nothing more than a modest range of hills, but presently you see that you're approaching a mountain wall several miles high. You look in vain for any pass or valley through which you can penetrate—and then, with a sick feeling in the pit of your stomach, you realize that your driver is making a frontal assault on that titanic barrier.

Ahead of you, the ground tilts abruptly in a slope as steep as the roof of a house. There's a sudden deepening in the vibration of the motors and then, scarcely checking its speed, the great bus charges up the endless, rock-strewn escarpment that seems to stretch ahead of you all the way to the stars.

Of course, there's no danger. This drive would be impossible on Earth, but here, under a sixth of Earth's gravity, there's nothing to it.

Presently, when you've been climbing for many minutes, you look back across the great plain over which you've been traveling. As more and more of the crater wall comes into view, you see that it's built up in a series of vast terraces, the first of which you've just surmounted. In a few minutes you reach the crest, and turn along it instead of descending into the valley ahead. Far to the south, you can see the great crescent of Earth hanging low above the mountains. It's a blinding blue-green as its clouds and oceans reflect the sunlight back to you across a quarter of a million miles of space. When it is full, it will be far too bright to look at comfortably without tinted glasses.

It takes nearly two hours to reach the outer rim of the crater, two hours of doubling back and forth along great valleys, of exhilirating and terrifying charges up those impossible slopes. At last the whole of the walled plain lies spread out beneath you, and you can see once again the buildings of the colony, dwarfed by distance and with a tiny, toylike spaceship standing beside them.

You can travel more swiftly now, for the downward slopes are much less steep than those inside the crater, as is usually the case on the Moon. Even so, it's another two hours before you've finished the descent and are out in open country again.

One gets used to anything in time, even to driving across the Moon. The seasoned travelers have long ago settled down to conversations and games of cards, interrupted only when it is time for meals. At last, the featureless landscape now flowing uneventfully past lulls you to sleep. You operate the lever that turns your chair into a couch, and settle down for a nap.

You awake hours later, when the tilt of the bus tells you that you are climbing again. It's quite dark: the blinds have been drawn to keep out the sunlight still blazing from the velvet sky. Everyone is asleep; apart from the vibration, and the tilt of the floor, you might be back on Earth in an airliner flying through the night. Presently, the steady throb of the motors sends you to sleep once more.

The next time you wake the blinds are up, sunlight is shining into the cabin, and there's a pleasant smell of cooking from the little galley. The bus is moving rather slowly along the crest of a long range of hills, and you're surprised to see that all the other passengers are clustered around the observation window at the rear. Naturally, you go to join them.

You look back across the miles of land through which you have been traveling during your sleep. When you last saw it, Earth had been hanging low in the southern sky —but where is it now? Only the silver tip of its great crescent still shows above the horizon; while you've been sleeping, it's been dropping lower and lower in the sky.

You're passing over the rim of the Moon, into the mysterious, hidden land where the light of Earth never shines, the land that, before the coming of the rocket, no human eyes had ever seen.

What will you discover there? Today, we don't know. It must be admitted that there is no reason to suppose that conditions are any different on the hidden face of the Moon than on the side we can see. Yet it's certainly tantalizing to think that almost half of our nearest neighbor in space is permanently turned away from us so that we can't see it.

There's a simple reason for this odd state of affairs. Millions of years ago the Moon did revolve so that the whole of its surface could be seen from Earth. However, as it turned, great tides were raised in the Moon's partly plastic substance by our planet's attraction, and those tides acted in much the same way as the brake shoes on a wheel. Slowly, over the ages, they brought the Moon to rest, until now it remains with the same face turned always towards us.

We should get some pictures of the hidden other side by means of radio-controlled rockets long before men actually land on the Moon. And don't, by the way, make the rather common mistake of thinking that the other side of the Moon is dark! It gets just as much sunlight as this side.

But its long nights must be lonely, for there is no brilliant Earth in the sky to illuminate the silent landscape. The first explorers to go around the rim of the Moon will feel much further away from home than those who only have to look up into the sky to see the familiar continents of their own planet . . .

10 - To the Planets

WHEN we start looking further afield than the Moon and begin to consider the problem of reaching the planets, we make a surprising and encouraging discovery. Though the distances involved are often several hundred—or even thousand—times as great, interplanetary voyages require little more fuel than lunar ones. The reason for this is the fortunate fact, which we have already mentioned, that once you have built up any speed in space there is no resistance to destroy it again. If you simply sit back and wait, you will reach your destination in due course, assuming, naturally, that you have started off in the right direction!

There is one snag, though. Such journeys may not require much energy, but they consume a lot of time. The trip to the Moon takes less than five days—and only two or three if one starts with a little extra speed. However, the voyage to Venus, if you are trying to save fuel by taking the most economical path, lasts 145 days. The journey to Mars is even longer, about 250 days. It would certainly be boring to spend all that time in space, though

it would probably be no worse than spending a winter
snowed up in the Antarctic, as many polar explorers have
done. A more serious objection is that such long journeys
would use up a considerable amount of food and oxygen
and thus make the supply problem difficult. And, of course,
the longer one spends in space, the greater the chances of
something going wrong—not to mention the danger of
meteors and cosmic rays.

It might be thought that it would be easiest to travel
to the planets when they were at their nearest. Actually,
the precise opposite is the truth. This is because when
the planets are closest to Earth they are moving past us—
or we are moving past them—at very great speeds. For
example, the speed of the Earth in its orbit around the Sun
is 66,000 miles an hour; Venus moves a good deal faster,
at 78,000 miles an hour. If we want to move from Earth to
Venus, therefore, we must somehow compensate for this
difference of speed.

It turns out that the most economical way to do this is
to let the spaceship fall in towards the Sun in such a way
that it overtakes Venus, as shown in the diagram (Figure
6). When the spaceship leaves Earth, it fires its rockets for
a few minutes to put it into the right orbit, and the Sun's
gravity field does the rest. The ship becomes, in fact, a
new planet for five months, and at the end of that time it
will automatically arrive (if the original navigation was
correct) at the orbit of Venus. The rockets then have to
be fired for a few minutes to match the ship's speed to that
of Venus, and then a landing can be made. The rockets
might be firing for less than ten minutes on a journey that

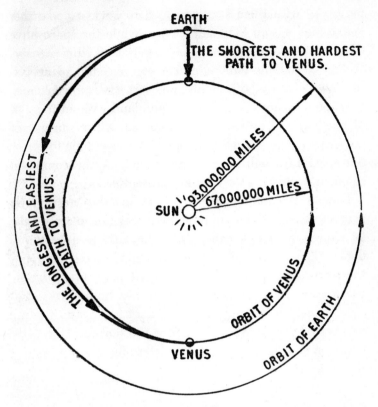

Fig. 6.　The voyage to Venus.

lasted 145 days! This is quite typical of the sort of thing that will happen in astronautics.

It is very unlikely that any interplanetary journey, for a long time to come, will start directly from the surface of the Earth. Because of the fuel required, as well as for other technical reasons, interplanetary spaceships will begin their voyages from an orbit around the Earth, in the way we have already described for the lunar journey. They may take with them small, winged rockets to make the actual landings on Mars and Venus, while the spaceships themselves take up orbits—like those described earlier for the space-stations circling Earth—around the planet of destination. Since both Venus and Mars have atmospheres, we should be able to glide down and land without the use of much rocket power. This, of course, will mean a tremendous saving of fuel; and, since for a long time to come our spaceships will have to carry fuel for the complete round trip, this is a very important matter.

How is the pilot going to direct his ship accurately across so many millions of miles of space? Fortunately, this is a question which can already be answered in some detail. The science of "astronavigation"—navigation by the stars—has been highly developed here on earth for use at sea. By observing the heavenly bodies with his sextant (which is simply an instrument for measuring the number of degrees they are above the horizon) the captain of a ship in mid-ocean can determine his position to within a mile.

The same methods will be used in space, though the instruments will be somewhat more complicated—and so will the calculations. The navigator of the spaceship, however, will have one great advantage which the captain of an ocean liner groping through fog might well envy. He will always be able to observe all the stars and planets, for there will never be any clouds to obscure his view. What is more, he will be able to see the complete skyful of stars, something we can never do here on Earth, where the ground beneath our feet cuts off half the sky.

We should remember that even if the pilot makes a small

mistake during the initial pull-away from Earth, he will be able to correct it later. For the spaceship can be steered, and its velocity altered, by further use of the rockets at any time. However, because it takes so much fuel to make a major change in direction, it is essential for the navigation to be as precise as possible. A really bad error at the start would mean that the ship might head off in a direction from which it could not get back to any planet on its existing fuel reserve. And that would be fatal, for there would be no hope of rescue except under very exceptional circumstances. The unfortunate crew would travel on through space until they ran out of food or oxygen. No doubt the navigator responsible would be the first to go through the airlock in order to conserve supplies . . .

It would be very important for spaceships, like airplanes, to be able to communicate with their base or their home planet. Many of the complicated navigational calculations might have to be carried out by giant electronic brains, and the results radioed to the pilots who had to use them. Also, quite apart from the practical value of good communications, it would be essential from the point of view of morale for ships to keep in touch with their bases during the weeks or months of their journeys. The crews would need some relaxation, and no doubt one day special programs will be broadcast from Earth to keep its far-flung children in touch with home.

We can send radio messages around the world—but that is a mere 25,000 miles. Can we keep in touch with spaceships not merely thousands but millions, perhaps hundreds of millions, of miles away? And in any case, can radio waves cross space?

The answer to both these questions is a firm "Yes." Perhaps the most dramatic proof of this was given in 1946, when the United States Army Signal Corps directed a short-wave radio beam to the Moon and got an echo back. The power needed to obtain an echo is thousands of times greater than that required merely to send a message in one direction, and almost any present-day radio transmitter could send a good signal to the Moon. All that would be necessary would be to use radio waves short enough to go through the reflecting Heaviside layer or ionosphere which surrounds the Earth.

To get messages to the planets, or to ships far away in space, it will be necessary to build rather large "radio mirrors" like the great concave reflectors used in some types of radar and the new science of radio-astronomy. These act very much like searchlights and concentrate all the radio waves in one direction (Plate 25). Even using the sort of equipment we have today, it would be possible to send speech for many millions of miles, and Morse signals (which require much less power) for hundreds of millions. And by the time we need such services, we can be sure that the radio engineers will have done even better!

Since radio waves travel at a speed of 186,000 miles a second, there would always be a time-lag before one could get a reply from anybody in space. At the Moon's distance, the delay is quite small—less than three seconds. For Mars and Venus, however, it would be several minutes even when they were closest to Earth; and it would take more than five *hours* for a radio signal to make the journey from Pluto.

Today, before we have built any spaceships at all, it is obviously impossible to guess how large or how swift they may ultimately become. But looking back and seeing how vessels of sea and air have developed, it seems safe to predict that the spaceships of a few centuries hence may carry very large numbers of people in perfect safety between the planets. They will be powered by atomic energy, perhaps operating some kind of electric rocket of the kind mentioned in Chapter 3. It is even possible that some new principle of propulsion may have been discovered, but that is pure guesswork. We know that the rocket can do the job; it will be nice if something better turns up, but if not we'll do without it.

Perhaps the real space-liners may spin slowly as they travel through space, to give the passengers a sensation of weight (Plate 26). This idea is attractive from some points of view, and it may prove essential if weightlessness has any dangerous effects. However, it would introduce complications of its own. One can well imagine a new kind of space-sickness being caused by the sight of the stars revolving completely around the sky every few seconds!

The first spaceships, as we have seen, will take several months to make the journeys even to the nearest planets. But, as for all other forms of transport, speeds will steadily increase. The long, lonely months of the first pioneers will be carved down to weeks, and eventually to days. There is no limit to speed in space, at least, according to Einstein's theory of relativity, not until one begins to approach the velocity of light. And as *that* is 670,000,000 miles an hour, it's not a speed limit that will worry us for a long time to come! At a thousandth of this velocity, one would get to Mars in a few days.

As greater speeds become available, they would not merely shorten the voyages to the nearer planets; they would also make it possible to travel to more distant worlds such as Jupiter and Saturn. Eventually, though this may well take several hundred years, spaceships from Earth will have reached all the planets of the Sun, from scorched Mercury to eternally frozen Pluto and the unknown worlds that may lie beyond it.

What will they find—and why will they go there? The time has come to try to answer these questions—though the real reasons for going to the planets we shall never fully know until we get there . . .

11 - Worlds of Tomorrow

IT HAS taken us a long time to realize that, in the solar system at least, there are no other planets like Earth. One of the lessons of modern astronomy is that you can forget all about the idea of walking around on another world just as you would here, breathing its air and perhaps meeting people very much like human beings. The facts are quite different—and may, in the long run, be considerably more interesting.

Ignoring distant Pluto, about which we know practically nothing, the planets fall into two sharply defined groups. First there are the four dwarfs—Earth, Venus, Mars, and Mercury—ranging in diameter from 8,000 miles for Earth down to 3,000 miles for Mercury, with Mars and Venus in between. After this there's a big jump in size when we come to the four giants—Jupiter, Saturn, Uranus, and Neptune. Jupiter is over *80,000* miles in diameter—that's ten times the diameter of Earth—and even the smallest of this group, Uranus, is over 30,000 miles through the center.

Quite apart from mere size, there's a fundamental differ-

ence between the giants and the dwarfs. For the Earth-
type dwarfs are solid, while the Jupiter-type giants are
not.

We're so used to our own solid Earth that it's difficult
to realize that our planet is probably a freak and is quite
overshadowed by worlds ten times bigger and of a completely different composition. Jupiter (Plate 27) and his
companions have enormously thick atmospheres which
get denser and denser towards the center of the planet
until eventually they become liquid at some unknown
depth. Down in those depths great eruptions or disturb-
ances sometimes take place, causing what one might call
storms, except that they are often bigger than our entire
world and sometimes last for years. It is highly unlikely,
therefore, that our spaceships will ever land on these inhospitable planets, whose atmospheres, incidentally, consist of poisonous gases such as methane, ammonia, and
hydrogen. But it will still be worth going out to visit
them, not only to observe them from really close quarters
but because they have at least 28 moons of assorted sizes,
and, on many of these, landings could undoubtedly be
made.

The giant planets are all at a great distance from the
Sun, and are therefore intensely cold. To them, our Sun
will be little more than a blinding star, giving practically
no heat. As one traveled out towards Neptune, one would
find that all the gases in the atmospheres of these planets
became first liquid, then solid, because of the low temperatures. On Pluto, the thermometer would never rise above
300 degrees below zero Fahrenheit.

One day, men will develop the engineering techniques

needed to explore the frigid moons of these outer worlds. Some of those moons, such as Titan, the largest satellite of Saturn, are as big as Mercury, and will probably be used as bases and refueling points for ships exploring the outer fringes of the solar system. It is even possible that, some day, we may send spaceships down into the turbulent atmospheres of the giant planets themselves—but they will be automatic survey vessels, without human crews.

Saturn, second largest of the outer planets, is famous for its unique system of rings, which makes it one of the most beautiful objects in the sky (Plate 28). Those rings puzzled early astronomers a good deal, but we know now that they consist of myriads of particles circling the planet in independent orbits, and so closely packed that they appear solid. One day, perhaps, our spaceships will enter those wonderful rings to discover what materials compose them. It would be safe to do this, because at any one point all the particles are traveling in the same direction and at the same speed. If a spaceship matched this speed, all the ring fragments around it would seem to be at rest, so the ship would appear to be in the middle of a motionless hailstorm. The analogy may be rather close, for it has in fact been suggested that the particles of the ring are composed of ice.

However, let us turn our eyes inwards to the warmth and light of the Sun, and see if we have better luck with our three neighboring worlds—Mercury, Venus, and Mars. We'll go to Mercury first, the nearest planet to the Sun.

Now we are at the other extreme from the outer worlds; it's a question of out of the refrigerator and into the fire! For Mercury is a little more than a third of Earth's distance from the Sun, and gets seven times as much heat. Things wouldn't be so bad, though, if the planet turned on its axis so that its whole surface was uniformly warmed by the Sun. As it is, one side freezes in perpetual darkness, while the other roasts in eternal day.

If you were at the center of Mercury's sunlit side, the rocks around you might be at a temperature of over 700° F.—hot enough to melt some metals. As you moved towards the dark side of the planet, and the Sun sank lower in the sky, the temperature would fall rapidly until there would be quite a wide belt where it was fairly temperate. Beyond this region, and covering half the planet, would be the frozen land of eternal darkness, lit only by the stars. Hanging in the sky one would often see the brilliant beacon that was our Earth, with a fainter star, the Moon, close behind it.

Because Mercury is a small world, its gravity is low, and a planet with a low gravity cannot keep an atmosphere, since its gases would leak away into space. Until recently, Mercury was thought to be quite airless, but now we know that it has a very thin atmosphere, certainly much too thin for us to breathe, even if it were made of oxygen.

Clearly, no creatures that exist on Earth could live on Mercury—but does that mean that life of any sort would be impossible there? We don't really know enough to answer that question, for life on *this* Earth is still very much of a mystery. It used to be thought, for example, that life could arise only on a planet that had oxygen in its atmosphere. We now know that this is wrong, because free oxygen does not occur in nature in any quantity.

It is actually produced by living things—plants—so the first forms of life on our planet must have been able to exist in an atmosphere with practically no free oxygen.

It does seem, however, that all forms of life need water in the liquid form, and that sets definite temperature limits. It is difficult to imagine plants or animals existing where it is so hot that all water is turned into steam, or so cold that it is permanently frozen. True, once life has evolved under fairly moderate conditions of temperature, it can learn to protect itself against cold and heat in very remarkable ways (look at the animals of the Arctic region, for example, not to mention the Eskimos!). But it must get started in the first place somewhere where the climate isn't too extreme.

On this argument, then, there would seem to be no reason why some form of life could not arise in the temperate zone of Mercury, and then extend (perhaps evolving into two completely different species) into the sunlit and also the night sides of the planet. But this is pure speculation. We won't know until we get there— which is one of the best reasons for going.

Between Earth and Mercury lies Venus, which has often been called Earth's sister world. The only reason for this is its size, just a little less than our planet's. That seems to be as far as the resemblance goes, for in every other respect Venus is most unlike Earth.

In the first place, her atmosphere is entirely different from ours—and here we are up against a major mystery. When you look at Venus through a telescope, the planet seems to be covered with a brilliant, unbroken white blanket. There are no markings at all, none of the divisions into continents and seas which would be so obvious to observers looking at Earth from space. Sometimes, faint and shadowy patches can be glimpsed, but even these are uncertain and they never last for long.

It is obvious, therefore, that we do not see the surface of the planet, but only the top of a thick layer of clouds which never, or hardly ever, breaks. When this was realized, it was natural to assume that the clouds were of the same kind as those found in our own atmosphere, and this in turn suggested that Venus was covered with great oceans and was, perhaps, a steamy, tropical sort of planet. On this argument, we might expect to find it inhabited by the sort of creatures that lived on Earth some millions of years ago: the giant reptiles who, luckily for us, passed away ages before man appeared on the scene. If this were true, Venus would be a veritable heaven for geologist, big-game hunter, and film producer.

Unfortunately, this exciting dream has been dissolved by the instruments of modern science. In the spectroscope, which analyzes the light we receive from the heavenly bodies, the astronomers have a means of determining what kind of gases make up the atmosphere of a planet. When the spectroscope was turned on Venus, it revealed no trace of water vapor, which would have been present if those brilliant clouds were the kind we have on Earth. Nor did it show any signs of oxygen. Instead, the Venusian atmosphere contains quite enormous quantities of the suffocating gas carbon dioxide.

Now this is the sort of atmosphere one might expect on a world where the first primitive plants were starting to evolve but animals had not yet emerged. So Venus may be too young even for dinosaurs; they may still lie a few hundred million years in the planet's future!

Carbon dioxide is a colorless, invisible gas, so this does not explain away the dazzling white clouds. Here, we simply have to admit ignorance, and to confess that we know more about planets ten times further away than we do about our second closest neighbor in space.

The temperature on Venus is probably not much higher than on Earth, because, though she is a good deal closer to the Sun, her clouds reflect a great deal of its heat back into space. There would certainly be no difficulty in finding regions of the planet where it was not too warm by our standards.

On the whole, it seems that we will not be able to discover much about Venus until we actually land there. Of course, before this is attempted there will be a close survey of the planet from space, and the dense atmosphere will be probed by radar beams and, later, by automatic rockets carrying TV equipment. It will be an exciting moment when the first spy-rocket breaks through the clouds and sends us its pictures of the unknown land beneath . . .

Now we'll swing outwards past the Earth's orbit to little Mars, in many ways the most interesting of all the planets. Its interest arises from the fact that it's the only planet whose surface we can see at all clearly. Mars has an atmosphere which is sometimes cloudy, but on the whole it seldom hides the features beneath.

A great deal of nonsense has been written about Mars, so let's start by getting a few facts straight. Under conditions of perfect visibility, and with the largest telescopes, we cannot see anything on the planet less than about twenty miles across. So we could hardly hope to detect cities as large as London or New York, let alone individual Martians, should any exist!

One's first view of Mars, even through a good telescope, is likely to be disappointing. All that can be seen is a small, not very clear disk, with a few dusky markings and a white spot at one side (Plate 29). However, by observing the planet patiently for many years, astronomers have built up remarkably detailed maps and have been able to learn a great deal about physical conditions on Mars.

It's a small planet, little more than half the diameter of Earth and with about a third of our gravity. And it's all dry land; there are no seas or lakes, and water appears to be very rare. At the poles are two white caps, which shrink during the summer in their respective hemispheres and grow again during the winter. Our Earth, seen from space, would have similar caps: the snows of the Arctic and Antarctic regions. The fact that the Martian polar caps sometimes disappear completely during the summer proves that they must be very thin, and they may consist of layers of frost only a few inches deep. So they cannot be compared with the thick icecaps of Earth.

There's an atmosphere, but one thinner than at the top of our highest mountains. You would have to go up into our stratosphere before you found pressures as low as at the surface of Mars. The atmosphere is probably mostly nitrogen, and contains no oxygen that can be measured by our spectroscopes. So we must write off Mars, like all the other planets, as the abode of life of the kind we know.

Yet, almost certainly, there is life there. Mars has seasons just as the Earth has (though they are almost twice as long) and large areas of the planet around the equator change color in the spring and summer in the way one would expect vegetation to behave. It must be vegetation of a very odd kind, perhaps not unlike the lichens which may be found on weathered rocks.

Because of its greater distance from the Sun, Mars is a good deal colder than the Earth. Its thin atmosphere is also a much less effective "heat blanket," and for this reason the planet's nights and winters are very cold indeed. They are not so cold, however, that suitably evolved life-forms could not hibernate through them.

Beyond this, there is no evidence at all for the existence of animal life, still less intelligent life, on Mars. At the beginning of the century there was much speculation about the so-called canals on the planet, markings which some astronomers considered too straight to be natural. However, though there are undoubtedly some curious lines on Mars, very few astronomers today take seriously the idea that they are artificial.

We may be able to discover what they are when we can get telescopes above the atmosphere, in the space-station observatories, and can thus have infinitely clearer views than are possible from the surface of the Earth. People often ask: "Why can't you use the giant new telescopes like the 200-inch reflector on Mount Palomar to settle the question?" The answer is that such telescopes cannot use greater magnifications than instruments a tenth of the size, because of the unsteadiness of our atmosphere. They are built to see very faint and distant objects which smaller instruments cannot detect. In other words, they

are designed for *light-gathering* power, rather than mag·
nification. It must also be confessed that few professional
astronomers are very much interested in the planets these
days. They are more concerned with other universes millions of light-years away, and not with our next-door
neighbors only *light-minutes* away across the road! The
big telescopes are therefore fully booked up for other
work and are seldom available for observing the planets.

In 1956 Mars will be nearer the Earth than it has been
for many years, and the 200-inch telescope may be used to
photograph the planet if conditions are favorable. It would
be unwise, however, to expect any spectacular results.

We would like to know a great deal more about Mars
than we do, but nevertheless it has taught us one lesson
of immense value. On a world where conditions are much
more severe than here, life seems to have gained a foot-
hold. One day, not so far in the future, we'll find just
what kind of life that is.

12 · The Challenge of the Planets

MANY people, when they hear what alien conditions we shall encounter on the other planets, are inclined to ask: "Why bother about space-flight if things are so unpleasant outside the Earth?" That's a good question, and one that must be answered convincingly.

There are many reasons why explorers have endured great hardships and often given their lives to reach out-of-the-way places on this Earth. Curiosity alone isn't the only answer, though it is an important one. The men who finally conquered Mount Everest knew that they would make no wonderful discoveries when they reached the summit: the top of one mountain is much the same as that of any other. But, as long as Everest remained unclimbed, it was a challenge—a challenge that had to be met for its own sake. That most people feel this way was proved by the enormous pride and interest aroused by the mountain's conquest.

The planets represent a similar challenge. Even if there were no practical value in going to them, men would certainly cross space as soon as it became technically possible to do so. There are a lot of places on this Earth that are not worth visiting—but people have been there just to make sure!

However, travel into space will be very much worthwhile, even though at the present time we can guess at only a few of the things that may be discovered on the other planets. We have already seen how astronomy will make tremendous advances as soon as we can lift our telescopes above the atmosphere, and there is hardly a single branch of science that will not make giant steps forward when the conquest of space begins. It is just because conditions *are* so different on the other planets that we may expect to make new discoveries there. Even if we do not encounter the weird life-forms beloved by science-fiction writers, there will still be enough to keep geologists, physicists, and chemists busy for centuries.

But what use is scientific knowledge? Well, in the first place, it is valuable for its own sake: it enables us to have a better understanding of our place in the universe, and it satisfies that curiosity which, more than anything else, distinguishes Man from the animals. All the greatest scientists sought knowledge simply because they wanted to know, not because they were looking for something of practical value.

Yet, of course, scientific knowledge *is* of enormous practical value: our whole civilization, all the machines we use, the clothes we wear, the food we eat, the entertainment we see on TV or motion-picture screen, the drugs we take when we are ill—all these things are the result of scientific discoveries. All things that increase knowledge also increase power; one must understand the universe before one can do anything about it. It is true that knowledge can be used for good or evil, but that is a moral problem, not a scientific one. The scientist is not responsible for the fact that the study of bacteria can give us both penicillin and germ warfare.

We will discover many strange and valuable minerals on the planets, and when space-flight is sufficiently far advanced it will be worthwhile bringing them back to Earth to replace our own diminishing resources. But, in the long run, our most precious import from space will be a greater understanding of the strange universe in which we live.

To what extent the other planets will be actually colonized by people from Earth, it is quite impossible to predict. Until we have discovered a great deal about them by direct exploration, we will obviously not know which planets are worth developing, and which will be left alone. There is no doubt that, even with the knowledge we have today, it would be possible to maintain bases on the Moon and the nearer planets.

Engineers and architects have already amused themselves by considering some of the problems that will have to be met when we attempt to construct the sort of lunar base mentioned in Chapter 9. The Moon, having no atmosphere at all, represents rather an extreme case, but similar difficulties would have to be overcome on planets like Mars and Venus, which have unbreathable atmospheres. Our first bases here might be constructed from flexible domes, blown up by the air pressure inside them. They would, in fact, be rather like giant balloons, which could be easily carried and then inflated on arrival. Entry

and exit would, of course, be through airlocks. Small experimental "buildings" of this kind have already been
made for special purposes (Plate 30) and because they
do not require any supporting pillars—the internal air-
pressure holds up the entire weight—they could be of
enormous size if necessary. Large enough, perhaps, to en-
close entire cities, when the time comes to build cities on
Mars or Venus . . .

Fantastic? Certainly not, when one thinks of all that
has happened in the last hundred years, and remembers
that thousands—indeed, millions—of years lie ahead of us.

One day, all the planets of the Sun will have been explored, just as all the Earth is today. Mars, Venus, Ganymede, Titan, Phobos will be names as familiar as New
Zealand, Canada, Peru, South Africa—countries which
were once unknown, which once took longer to reach than
will the planets a hundred years from now. The frontier will
move outwards from Earth, past the frozen worlds at the
fringes of the solar system, until at last men are looking
out across the great abyss, with all the planets behind
and nothing between them and the incredibly distant stars.
Across that gulf, light itself, the fastest thing in the universe, takes years to travel. Yet out there must lie other
solar systems, some of them with planets much more like
Earth than are any of the other worlds of our own Sun.
And somewhere among the thousands of millions of stars
scattered throughout space there must, surely, be other
intelligent races, many of them far in advance of our own.
One day we shall meet them: it may not be for thousands
of years, but that is the ultimate goal of astronautics.

We may never actually meet them face to face; contact

may be made by automatic spaceships that will return to Earth many generations after they have set out, bringing back the knowledge their cameras and recorders have obtained. Or perhaps medical science may discover ways of permitting the spaceship crews to "hibernate," so that they may be able to travel on journeys lasting for centuries. Or perhaps, though all the evidence is against it, the speed of light may prove to be no greater obstacle than the speed of sound, so that we may achieve such velocities that men will be able to travel to the stars and return in a single lifetime.

We do not know—but we can be sure that, even if we never reach the stars, the planets of our own solar system will keep all our scientists and explorers busy for as far ahead as imagination can go.

13 - The Road Ahead

IN THE last chapter, we looked a long way ahead and touched on scientific achievements that none of us will live to see. Yet in the near future we may expect to watch the first man-carrying rockets climb to the limits of the atmosphere and beyond; and before 1975 automatic missiles should have entered orbits around the Earth and possibly landed a few pounds of radio equipment on the Moon. Thereafter, the crossing of space will become technically possible just as soon as the necessary effort and resources are devoted to it.

If unlimited funds were made available, and the project went ahead on a super-priority basis like the building of the atomic bomb, then it is possible that we might be able to get a spaceship on the Moon in about ten years. But there are some things that no amount of money can speed up, and the conquest of space will involve long and complicated experiments which will consume a great deal of time. Many of these experiments are being carried out now in connection with supersonic flight, guided missiles, and similar projects, so that, when the time is ripe for the building of spaceships, much of the knowledge needed will be already available from other sources.

If one made a survey among scientists and engineers working in the rocket field, one would find very few who consider it likely that we will reach the Moon within the next thirty years; but most of them would agree that a landing is quite probable before the end of this century. Some also expect the exploration of the nearer planets to have begun before the year 2000 dawns.

It is always possible, of course, that some new invention, perhaps an application of atomic power, may make space-flight practical at an earlier date. But this is pure speculation: we can be sure that the rocket can eventually do the job, but we cannot be sure when anything better will come along to replace it.

The date when space will be crossed does not depend on the scientists and engineers alone. They will only show *how* to do it—but nothing will happen until people and governments realize that it is worth doing, and provide the necessary resources. For this reason the many books and films that are now appearing on the subject of space-flight are doing valuable propaganda, even if they are only intended as entertainment. They are preparing the public to accept the idea of space-flight, in a way that it was never prepared for the arrival of aviation.

There are many young people nowadays who are anxious to play a part in the development of space-travel; perhaps you are one of them yourself, and want to know the best way to set about it. Well, you must recognize right away that there is no easy road, and that in this field, as in any other, years of hard work and study are necessary. Even then, the number of people who can make possible such great advances as, for example, Frank Whittle did in jet-propulsion, will always be rather small!

Astronautics, when it starts to develop ten or twenty years from today, will embrace so many different branches of science and technology that one could specialize in almost any subject and still contribute something to the crossing of space. Electronics, chemistry, aerodynamics, pure mathematics, astronomy, medicine, structural engineering, metallurgy, nuclear physics—all these and many more will be involved in the building of successful space-ships. So your choice is a wide one, but whatever subject you specialize in you must remember this: you may have to wait a good many years before you can use your knowledge in anything so exciting as the building of a real space-ship! Fortunately, however, the skills that will be involved in astronautics are also in great demand elsewhere in our modern world—in aviation, to take an obvious example—so that anyone who possesses them can always be assured of employment.

So to those who hope that they may one day pioneer on this great new frontier, we would say this: Study hard at scientific subjects, and follow whatever practical hobby you can (for example, astronomy with home-made tele-scopes, building model aircraft and radios). Then, having specialized in technical subjects at school, either take a science or engineering degree at college, or else go into some industrial firm where you can get practical experi-ence and continue spare-time studies through the appren-

tice training schemes which are now widely available.*
And, of course, read all you can about space-flight: there
are many books on the subject, some of them quite advanced. Even if they aren't on the library shelves, your
local librarian can usually help you obtain them. Here are
some examples to start with, which will lead you on to
further reading:

Clarke, Arthur C. *The Exploration of Space.* Harper &
Brothers, 1951.

Ley, Willy. *Rockets, Missiles and Space Travel.* Viking
Press, 1947.

Ley, Willy, and Bonestell, Chesley. *The Conquest of Space.*
Viking Press, 1949.

Ryan, Cornelius. (ed.) *Across the Space Frontier.* Viking
Press, 1952.

The third of these books contains some marvelous paintings showing what we believe it to be like on the surface
of the Moon and planets. One day, if the present rate of
scientific progress continues, *you* may be able to compare
them with the reality . . .

* For further advice, see the leaflet *Careers in Astronautics* by A. V.
Cleaver, F.R.Ae.S., which may be obtained from the British Interplanetary Society at 12, Bessborough Gardens, London, S.W.1.

WISCONSIN STATE COLLEGE
EAU CLAIRE, WISCONSIN
LIBRARY RULES

No book should be taken from the library until it has been properly charged by the librarian.

Books may be kept ~~two~~ *one* weeks but are not to be renewed without special permission of the librarian.

A fine of two cents a day will be charged for books kept over time.

In case of loss or injury the person borrowing this book will be held responsible for a part or the whole of the value of a new book.

MIRANDA'S MUSIC

Miranda's Music

By Jean Boudin
and Lillian Morrison

DRAWINGS
BY HELEN WEBBER

Thomas Y. Crowell Company
NEW YORK

Contents

To Jo and Janice
and
To Leonard and Kenneth

Hi, Mike

If

If only I had three wishes
one of them would be not
to do the dishes

The other two
would be you

April

The spring tree pops cracker jack leaf buds
outside our window
there is a prize in the box
the blood races greenily
I am dancing with fancy a queen in your arms
and mother talks of spring cleaning.

Question

How will you love me
What shall I say think wear
Smell of what flowers?
Do you think I should thank you
Or quickly embrace
If when you walk in the door
You hand me a gift—
Or stand speechless staring
At your face?

At First Sight

I lived on a rooftop
among the aerials.
The street was all eyes and intersections.

One day I saw you
and came down.
Parties going on in all directions.

The Prince

I cannot play chess

  Feel sure I'm a mess

I cannot play tennis

  My sister's a menace

Am a mediocre dancer

  She has all the answers

Spend hours at the dentist

  I haven't the faintest

Cannot carry a tune

  Idea when he'll come

Sometimes I write poems

  But I know I will know him

See-er

By the flick of a buttercup
under your chin with
the sun half in shadow
whether or not you like butter
I become a diviner

Unspelled

It is over.
The script uncurls
And I skip rope
In the unraveled letters
Of your name.
The line whips
The ground fast
Salt Vinegar Mustard Pepper
I jumpjumpjump
It's the only thing to do
With you.

Triolet

I took it to heart,
It didn't do well there.
I wasn't so smart,
I took it to heart.
Hard and apart,
It holed up in a shell there.
I took it to heart,
It didn't do well there.

Weaving

hand lacing   word knitting
the net of sweethearting
unraveling no's

tying knots and   bows

Who Am I?

Who Am I?

I
a
m

m
u
s
c
l
e
s

and answers

Like animals   and dancers.

Special

I am all made up of matter
and energy and
you too, you too

But not a single cell of them
can think they think
or feel their

Feelings as I do, we do.

Miranda on Sixth Avenue

It's music that she wishes.
She hears it all the time
So let her dance
The drum road
Windingly.
   Pavane or pirouette
    To secret chimes
Do sarabande
To chords and thuds
To exclamations
From the orange-hatted chorus
In the subway excavations.

On Stage

if applause
    had no pause
  I'd curtsey and nod
            endlessly

Status

I want most to
be the best

The rest of you
can be the rest

But oh the judgment
and the test.

Creation

I am because I
Think I am
A yam.
If I sit in water
In the sun
It is my belief
I will flower and leaf
In sprawling curling
Vine.

Moods and Weather

Good Morning

Some mornings I wake up with poems
pushing
        to get out after the night

's crowding into light from

under the covers before the cold

air.

Storm

If trees are black at night
who is there to say
they are green by day

or know whiteness

covers them with snow autumn
with brightness. I will not
go on kneeling to tendrils

greèning springing

April lovers clinging
One thing left
to answer back

Black Black Black

At the Subway Entrance

If in this diffident winter sun
I drift a little
will I be forgiven?

Tendered with milky sunshine
shriven
if I could hail a cab and ride

in the mistbright
wrong direction that
that would be heaven

A Simple

kill or cure's too Simon pure for
me
Simon had his illnesses and well
nesses
penny or not the pieman's pie may
sour
sometimes there is no fair

day you
   are a gray silk
      dress with green leaves

to try on
   through the slats
      in my Venetian blind

prison you are
   clammy with green
      leaves of parsley and

no sun
   now you have crawled over
      my head

a humid sheath   staying
   my plans of whom we shall seize
      together

or shall
   we stay here, I mulling
      you wraithing

day you
   are a gay silk
      dress with green leaves

to try on shining
   through the slats
      in my Venetian striped

prism you are
   of yellow melon
      and of lemon

playing sun
   now you shimmer over
      my head

a warm sheath staying
      my plans of whom we shall please
        together

or shall
   we stay here, I mulling
      you wreathing

Dull Drums

      Light, crawl through
      crawl through that
      crawl through that hole
      crawl through that pile of rock
      crawl through that long dark winding cave
      where I am sitting.

Saturday Morning

Thank you for making
The green leaves half turn orange
Thank you, all of you, who so long ago and
     presently,
Despite your devotion to pounding
Cement on earth
Brick on brownstones
Whirling wheels on streets
Laying pipes beneath
And running subways underground
Still left the ginkgo tree around
Outside my window.
Thank you, Henry, for washing the
Windows clean, easy as a dancer in your
Perilous imbalance on a six-inch window sill
For now
The tree's colors
Can be clearly seen varying
In the dancing shade and glare
Of light and breeze.

Best Friend

Stella
appropriately
is fond of
astronomy
takes photographs
of starfish,
and has green stars
for eyes
at home in skies
where tigers walk
on clouds.

Proposal

Life sometimes I love you.
Let us settle down and
Live together for better
And for worse.
It is only through us
The stone feels warm in the sun.

Lessons

Song

lyric are
      my
           feelings
dressed up
      in
          letters
of an alphabet
   dancing around
  in

           in
  sound
           sound
a musical note cannot vote
but it may sway a crowd

Science Fiction

I find hearts
are rarely welcome
in the parlors of

the mind
going

from the sublime
to the meticulous
confines the

cyto-
plasm

cytoplasm occupies
the region between
the nucleus

and
the

cell membrane
as I've told you again
and again

Rune

Don't kill time,
Don't mark time.

In the full time
Spill time.

In the dark time
Spark time.

To Whooo

Young are the songs
    of right and wrong
and cruel cruel and
    foolish

Wise are the sighs
    of compromise
    and owlish

Lab Babble

To be both physicist and anarchist
Is unity of extremes
As you are you in even your wildest dreams
As you are you
As you can be east and west by whirling.

Track down cracks in a silicon of sand.
Splice the spilling schemes of the ungoverned.

Non / sense

> A fog / is not / a frog / is not
> A bog / is not / desira / ble
> Nor is / a trim tetrim / eter
> Practi / cal or
> Logical.

Tell Me

Do clouds mean more
Than grammar to
A monkey in the zoo?
Which to you?

I do not mean to ask for
The meaning of meaning
Only the more or less of it
The bars of compromise.

SOME OF MY TEACHERS
have frozen faces,
fortifications in use,
the freeze
lending a stark grandeur
to the face scape,
a defined outline
to the face shape.
One looks into the eyes and sees
a bobcat
in the Bastille, a poodle
on Mount Everest.

Coincidences

We do not die
of joy that's

just an expression

nor does our heart
overflow without

serious consequences

bursting with energy
is first base and first place

fly and funny

both end in y
and why too.

Mike's Tune

Drum Solo

I'm a sharpshooter
    with a fly swat
I'm a spark footer
    in a jog trot
I'm a scar brooder
    but I try not
I'm a star mover
    with a sky mop.

Tennis Clinic

There was a young man from Port Jervis
Who developed a marvelous service
But was sorry he learned it
For if someone returned it
It made him impossibly nervous.

Miranda Guru

I meditate Miranda
She is fair
She binds me with a cord of
Braided blond
That swings
Me counter clockwise
Hanging there in clover only her
Love can sever me

The A—Train

I sail home on crescendos
Straphanging, scale home
On wailing rails and shrilling whistles
Look, man, one hand!
Now skate along smooth grates
Rockety   rocking   faster
Swacketing down the track
(O shrieking screamer streaming down)
Held swinging in the growing dying roars.

If I sit
    in your living room
        all evening
   grinning
     it is only because
       I am foolish
  about you.
     When I leave
        I skitter
         and bounce
    floating
     on every gusty thought
    that sails me
      zigzag
       home
        high
      on the very i-
       dea of you.

. . . . *Down*

I ate.
The food was great, Miranda
                    You, too

            but for you
                    I'm just not there
            so what to do but

    look in your eyes that swim away
                shake hands at the door
                in farewell

        and fall
                over
            the

        stairwell.

On the Beach

A falling star
landed here
in the mud, spraying sparks.

Life began,
caught on.
Funny stars all over the place now.

I walk among
showers of them
shooting from between your eyelashes.

Burning Bright

A mermaid's tears have
Silver fish in them,
A tiger's,
Yellow stars.
Mine have spikes and
Spokes of bikes
And yours have
Blue guitars.

Not on the Rocks

Something always the matter with mermaids
(who cannot walk) and so its talk
talk talk no ball games no

swimming no running. Just always sunning
in a beach chair   but its true
about their hair

The Racers

Skittish,
we flex knees, drum heels and
shiver at the starting line

waiting the gun
to pour us over the stretch
like a breaking wave.

Bang! We're off
careening down the lanes,
each chased by his own bright tiger.

Summer Times

Sea Song

Rich in the rocking bays,
Fat in the lapping waves,
Little yachts go skimming nip and tuck.

Trim in the snapping sun,
One with the swooping gulls,
Slim patrician sailboats dip and duck.

Now higher than the sky,
(Wind slapping swiftly by)
Pure and pouring water lifts them up.

New at the Lake

    There is an orange
       August moon bulging soft
         and uncertain

    Eyeing me through summer's
       floating by in dark lazy
         clouds, winds

    Dance with the trees
       on water, I wonder
         who lives next door.

Mooning

My tiger strikes with light
      On nights of blackest velvet
    Through slits of trees his eyes
        Are laser beams of summer

Lobster Cove Shindig

If there's a wind, we get it
Straight from the shoulder of rock
Bowling over boulders
Racketing through the house
Spray steaming mists rolling
Daisies ducking in the hullabaloo.
What a brawl until the sun appears
Majestic, like the law.

City Summer

The gas and the oil
Doughnuts, soot bits, peanuts,
Cigarette butts, all the perfumes of
     dime store Arabia
On a hot summer day in the subway,
Weight the sighs
Of subway riders
Wet with sweat.

Violets and buttercups almost
never come up, but in a window box,
a flower store or lyric.
Of little smell they swell the pages
     of a book of verse
With color.

Tall squares and verticals
Loom into the evening of a sky
Gleaming with Consolidated Edison's
     beseeching
Sea and ski
Sea and ski
Sea and ski

Air Traveler

He comes from afar
In a silver cigar
      And
         walks
            down
                the
                    ramp
Like a heavyweight champ.

Love Fifteen

Swing to wallop
and stretch to smash
the bounding ball,
O whip it down
and cover the ground
easily, lightly.

Smack the serve
and swift return,
stroke it fine,
drive it deep,
slam the lob's
looping flight,
Whang!

Here within
the chalked white
boundaries of
a sunny world
test with zest,
the body's wit
the body's reach
the body's might

Dancers in a
rigorous rite
who with every
ardent motion
praise the dark
and primal pulse
that pounds and bounces
in the light.

By the Seaside

I like the feel of breezes
    through my toes. I like the
feel of sneezes through my
    nose. I even like the feel

of tweezers if it makes my
    eyebrows please you and most
to hold your hand, walking
    in the sand along the water.

The Collector

Catches the towering wave
In cups of foam
And takes them home.

INDEX

ABOUT THE AUTHORS

JEAN BOUDIN is originally from Philadelphia. She was graduated from the University of Pennsylvania where she majored in English and Latin.

When Mrs. Boudin was nine years old, she composed a poem in honor of her aunt's engagement. Her uncle-to-be was so pleased that he rewarded her with a double-decker ice-cream cone. She has been writing poetry ever since.

Many of Mrs. Boudin's poems have appeared in newspapers and literary magazines. She is a recipient of the Dylan Thomas Poetry Award.

Jean Boudin now lives in New York City with her husband and their two children.

LILLIAN MORRISON was born and grew up in Jersey City, New Jersey. She was graduated Phi Beta Kappa from Douglass College and took her graduate degree in library science from Columbia University.

Miss Morrison's poems have appeared in the *Atlantic Monthly, Prairie Schooner, Poetry Northwest,* and other periodicals. She is the author of *The Ghosts of Jersey City and Other Poems* and compiler of *Sprints and Distances,* an anthology of poems about sports. As a librarian, author, and editor, Lillian Morrison has worked with young people for a number of years. In addition to her duties as librarian, she is general editor of the Crowell Poets, and she has compiled five popular collections of folk rhymes for young people.

Lillian Morrison makes her home in Manhattan.

ABOUT THE ILLUSTRATOR

HELEN WEBBER was particularly happy to work on this book, for she has been interested in poetry ever since her fourth-grade teacher "liberated her pupils from the conception that poetry has to rhyme." Mrs. Webber attended school in New York City and was graduated from Queens College. She studied social work at Columbia University and received a master's degree in art education at the Rhode Island School of Design.

Helen Webber's interests are varied. She has designed silk-screen wall hangings, paper napkins, toys, record covers, and book jackets, and she has written and illustrated several books for children. Her paintings and fabric collages have been exhibited in New England and New York City.

Mrs. Webber and her family live in San Diego, California.